Tommie L. Duncan is Chaplain Di-
rector at the United States Public
Health Service Hospital, Fort Worth,
Texas. He is the first full-time chaplain
to hold that position. A graduate of
Texas Lutheran College and Perkins
School of Theology, Southern Metho-
dist University, he took Clinical
Training at Terrell State Hospital and
Austin State Hospital, both in Texas.
Mr. Duncan serves on the Advisory
Board of Who's Who in American
Correction and is past president of the
American Protestant Correctional
Chaplains Association.

UNDERSTANDING
AND HELPING
THE NARCOTIC ADDICT

SUCCESSFUL PASTORAL COUNSELING SERIES

UNDERSTANDING AND HELPING THE NARCOTIC ADDICT

TOMMIE L. DUNCAN

PRENTICE-HALL, INC. ENGLEWOOD CLIFFS, N. J.

Understanding and Helping the Narcotic Addict,
by Tommie L. Duncan

© 1965 by Prentice-Hall, Inc., Englewood Cliffs, New Jersey.
Library of Congress Catalog Card Number: 65–11885

Printed in the United States of America.
T 93591

PRENTICE-HALL INTERNATIONAL, INC., *London*
PRENTICE-HALL OF AUSTRALIA, PTY., LTD., *Sydney*
PRENTICE-HALL OF CANADA, LTD., *Toronto*
PRENTICE-HALL OF INDIA (PRIVATE) LTD., *New Delhi*
PRENTICE-HALL OF JAPAN, INC., *Tokyo*

Drawings on pages 40 and 41 by Marie Hamlett

To
Don and Rose Marie Benton,
"who took the strangers in."

INTRODUCTION

This series of books represents the most comprehensive publishing effort ever made in the field of pastoral care. These books could not have been published twenty-five years ago or probably even ten, for the material was not then available. In the past, single books have been available covering different phases of the task. Now we are bringing the subjects together in a single series. Here we present a library of pastoral care covering the major topics and problems that most pastors will encounter in their ministry. Fortunately, not all of these problems need be faced every week or even every month. But, when they are, the minister wants help and he wants it immediately.

These books are prepared for the nonspecialized minister serving the local church, where he is the most accessible professional person in the community. It is a well-accepted fact that more people turn to clergy when in trouble than to all other professional people. Therefore, the pastor must not fail them.

Russell L. Dicks
General Editor

PREFACE

This volume is an attempt to answer some of the questions ministers ask about narcotic addiction.

Ministers whose interest in the narcotic drug problem is the result of national publicity given the matter by the various news media ask questions out of curiosity. Ministers who have narcotic addicts come to them for help ask questions out of necessity.

Some of the questions ministers have asked are: What kind of drugs are addicting? What effect do drugs have on the body and its functioning? Can anybody become addicted? How does a person become addicted? Where can the addict get medical treatment? What can the minister do for the addict?

Although the entire book deals with these questions, it is divided into two sections.

The first five chapters identify the addicting drugs, discusses their effect upon the individual, physically and emotionally, and describes various methods of using narcotic drugs. Included in this section is a chapter indicating the extremes to which an addicted person will go to obtain narcotic drugs. The final chapter in Section One attempts to correct some of the misconceptions about the addict.

Chapters five through ten deal more specifically with helping the addict. Consideration is given to the minister's initial contact with the addict, in terms of what to be aware of and what to do. Many have heard of the two Federal narcotic hospitals, but few actually know what takes place in them. In addition to a chapter on the Federal hospital treatment program, there is a chapter that discusses a few other groups that are interested in helping the addict. During the past six years, I have had occasion to visit several narcotic addict treatment centers to learn of their programs. In my opinion, anyone who assists in keeping addiction-prone persons free of drugs for any period of time has made a contribution. I have discussed only a few centers which may have come to the attention of the minister by way of recent publications and newspaper and magazine articles. The last chapter in the book lists specific needs of the former addict and suggests ways in which the minister may help.

This volume bears my name, but I cannot, in all honesty, claim credit for its creation. I have drawn from the experience of many persons who have worked with the addiction problem for many years.

I am deeply grateful to:

George E. Parkhurst, M.D., Chief of the Addiction Service, U.S. Public Health Service Hospital, Fort Worth, Texas, who for the past six years has been a guide and friend.

James F. Maddux, M.D., Medical Officer in Charge, U.S. Public Health Service Hospital, Fort Worth, Texas, who generously shared his grammatical talents by editing this manuscript.

Lee W. Weinrich, Information Officer, Division of Hospitals, U.S. Public Health Service, whose endorsement permitted the manuscript to be published.

More than one hundred theological students from several seminaries, who have studied the narcotic problem firsthand at the U.S. Public Health Service Hospital, Fort Worth, Texas, under the supervision of the author. Their numerous questions have validated the need for this book.

The men in my parish, about whom the book is written, for permission to use their comments, so that ministers might understand.

Sylvia, who typed the manuscript.

And Russell Dicks, who said, "I'm sure you can do it."

I hope in time there will be no need for a volume such as this. Until such a time when people turn to a Greater Source for the answer to life's problems, I pray that it will be a blessing.

"All things come of Thee, O Lord, and of Thine own have we given Thee."

T.L.D.

CONTENTS

CONTENTS

FOREWORD

Tommie Duncan has performed a real service for the pastoral care movement in writing this book, *Understanding and Helping the Narcotic Addict*. Since the pioneer work of Russell Dicks, Anton Boisen, and Seward Hiltner, the pastoral care movement has developed a whole new field of religious literature. This has been both extensive and significant; it has covered many subjects and many areas. Some excellent studies have appeared on subjects such as ministering to the sick, the alcoholic, and the family in need of counseling. In all the literature on pastoral counseling, pastoral care, and pastoral psychology we have no earlier study of the narcotic addict; in fact, only rarely has he been mentioned.

There is reason for this. Very few people know much of anything about the addict. This book will help to fill that gap.

This is a very practical book.

This is an informative book.

This is a realistic book.

This is a deeply spiritual book.

Chaplain Duncan writes from personal experience. He not only talks about ministering to the addict; he does it. Living in Fort Worth, I have had opportunity to know of the effectiveness of his ministry as Chaplain of the U.S. Public Health Service Hospital here. His writing embraces both a knowledge of the problem of addiction and an appreciation of the place of the pastor.

Although the average pastor will not meet this problem frequently, it can be a most complex and confusing experience when he does. He needs to know the nature of the problem, the approach to take, what to avoid, what resources are available, and the nature of his own role. This book will help him to understand these matters.

Charles F. Kemp

Brite Divinity School
Texas Christian University
Fort Worth, Texas

CHAPTER ONE

EFFECTS Of NARCOTIC DRUGS

In order to be conversant with the narcotic problem, the pastor needs to know something about narcotic drugs. He is probably not interested in becoming an expert, but at least he will want to know which drugs are addicting, what they do to the body, and what effect they have upon the emotions.

Since the beginning of time, man has sought relief from pain, both physical and mental. In his quest, he has tapped many sources—from the juices of various plants to voodoo. When he found something that worked, he used it, then looked for something better. He has never been content, for though man may devise methods and potions to ease physical pain, it is most difficult to deal with the pangs of emotional stress. The author is not sure that we are ever completely to be free from internal unrest, but he is confident that, if we are, the cure must be found in resolving the conflicts within ourselves —certainly not in the extracts of a plant.

Opium and its derivatives have powerful pain-killing ability. How long opium has been in use is difficult to determine. It is recorded on Assyrian medical tablets dated from the seventh century B.C. and on Egyptian Lists of Remedies of the sixteenth century B.C.; it was used by the Sumerians about 4000 B.C.[1]

Opium was thought to have miraculous qualities. In the second century, Galen wrote in his Eulogy of Opium:

"It resists poisons and venomous bites, cures inveterate headaches, vertigo, deafness, epilepsy, apoplexy, dimness of sight, loss of voice, asthma, coughs of all kinds, spitting of blood, tightness of breath, colic, the iliac poison, jaundice, hardness of the spleen, stones, uri-

[1] Herbert Yahraes, *Narcotic Drug Addiction,* U.S. Public Health Service Publication No. 1021 (Washington, D.C.: Government Printing Office, 1963), p. 1.

nary complaints, fevers, dropsies, leprosies, the troubles to which women are subject, melancholy, and all pestilences."

Opium does not have healing power over any maladies, but it can alter the emotional response to pain in such a manner that one doesn't care whether he is sick or not. Opium also makes a person feel sleepy and, taken in sufficient quantity, will put him to sleep. In the person who suffers from chronic depression or emotional tension or anxiety, opium relieves these troubled feelings and makes him feel good.

It has yet another quality, and this is what gives us concern. That is its addicting property. If the drug is taken in sufficient quantities over a given period of time, the body begins to crave it; without it, an uncomfortable reaction called "abstinence syndrome," or "withdrawal sickness," occurs.

In its raw state, opium is a thick, dark, sticky substance made from the juice of the incised, unripe seed capsule of the poppy plant. Seldom used in that form, it is therefore refined into morphine or changed into smoking opium. The use of smoking opium has just about disappeared in this country.[2]

Morphine, on the other hand, is one of our most popular analgesics and, under the direction of a competent physician, may be of inestimable value. First produced in 1817, this alkaloid possesses a combination of paralyzing and stimulating properties. It is dispensed in various forms—capsules, pills, powders, and solutions. Generally prescribed hypodermically by physicians, it is usually taken intravenously by the addict.[3]

Heroin, another derivative of opium, was discovered in 1898. Believed to be the ultimate for relief of pain, and nonaddicting, it was, moreover, advertised as a cure for morphine addiction. It was soon discovered that this was not the case. The white powdery substance could be used for the same purposes as morphine—and was several times as potent! Because of its strength it has since become a favorite of addicts. It can be diluted many times with milk sugar (for sales purposes) and still contain enough narcotic properties to produce

[2] D. P. Ausubel, *Drug Addiction* (New York: Random House, Inc., 1958), p. 16.
[3] Orin R. Yost, *The Bane of Drug Addiction* (New York: The Macmillan Company, 1954), p. 44.

sleep. The addicting properties of heroin led the United States Government to ban its use in this country.[4]

Heroin may be sniffed through the nose. Occasionally an addict will mix it with cocaine ("snow") and inject it in a vein, but it is generally mixed with water and taken intravenously by means of some crude hypodermic apparatus.

Synthetic narcotics are drugs that are made by chemical processes and are not opium derivatives. As well as the capacity to addict, many have morphine-like qualities for relieving pain. Two such drugs are meperidine and methodone.

Barbiturates constitute another large group of addicting drugs. Of recent emergence, the so-called "sleeping pills" were believed to be nonaddicting. It is now established that they are as addicting as some of the narcotic drugs. Since 1952, Federal law has regulated the interstate sale of these drugs. Seconal, nembutal, and phenobarbital, to name only three, are prescribed for a legion of aches and pains, tension, and insomnia.[5]

Bromides, although not as popular with physicians as they once were, are still prescribed on occasion to induce sleep. Not popular with addicts either, this group of drugs, although emotionally addicting, are not physically addicting, and therefore no withdrawal sickness occurs when dosage is abruptly stopped.[6]

Marihuana, though not physically addicting as are the opium derivatives or barbiturates, is by law an illegal drug. Made from crushed leaves and seeds of the hemp plant, rolled marihuana resembles tobacco, and is smoked after being rolled as a cigarette. It has no medical value whatsoever.

Alcohol in some circles is an approved beverage, yet for five million persons in the United States it has become an addicting agent that has completely bound them in its grasp. The alcohol problem is dealt with separately, and well it should be, for there are ninety-five times more alcoholics than persons addicted to all narcotic drugs.

Cocaine, a stimulant that is abused, has been used primarily as a local anesthetic to deaden pain in a certain area or organ without

[4] *Ibid.,* p. 45.
[5] *Ibid.,* p. 51.
[6] Victor H. and Virginia Vogel, *Facts About Narcotics* (Chicago: Science Research Associates, 1951), p. 15.

ADDICTING DRUGS	Causes emotional dependence	Causes physical dependence and withdrawal illness	Creates tolerance or a need for bigger doses
SEDATIVE OR NARCOTIC DRUGS (Relieve pain, cause mental and physical inactivity, have a numbing effect, produce sleep, and in larger doses cause stupor, coma, and death)			
OPIUM AND ITS PRODUCTS	Yes	Yes	Yes
Morphine			
Heroin			
Codeine			
Dilaudid			
Metopon			
Pantopon			
Paregoric			
Laudanum			
SYNTHETIC SUBSTITUTES FOR MORPHINE	Yes	Yes	Yes
Demerol			
Methadone			
BARBITURATES, "SLEEPING PILLS"	Yes	Yes	Yes
Luminal, phenobarbital			
Amytal			
Nembutal			
Seconal			
Barbital			
Pentothal			
BROMIDES	Yes	No	No
Nervino			
Neurosine			
Sodium bromide			
Potassium bromide			
Triple bromides			
Bromoseltzer			
MARIHUANA–INDIAN HEMP, "REEFERS," "MUGGLES"	Yes	No	No

ADDICTING DRUGS	Causes emotional dependence	Causes physical dependence and withdrawal illness	Creates tolerance or a need for bigger doses
STIMULANT DRUGS (Cause sleeplessness and excitement)			
COCAINE	Yes	No	No
BENZEDRINE-TYPE DRUGS	Yes	No	No
Benzedrine amphetamine			
Benzedrex			
Dexedrine			
Tuamine			
Desyphed			

Used with permission of: Science Research Associates, Chicago, Ill.

causing unconsciousness. It was applied directly to the eye in drops or by hypodermic injection elsewhere. For medical purposes, cocaine has been replaced by other drugs. Novocaine, one of the cocaine family, is used extensively by dentists to deaden gum sensation while working on the teeth.[7]

Aphetamine-type drugs, like cocaine, are frequently misused stimulants. They produce excitement, loss of appetite, and sleeplessness. Useful to persons who need a stimulant, or who may be reducing in weight under medical supervision, this group is very effective. These drugs, however, often are misused by the emotionally disturbed person who seeks a feeling of exhilaration, or the person who for one reason or another needs to stay awake for a prolonged period of time. The drug will produce insomnia. It does not increase a person's effectiveness.[8] These drugs are dangerous because they can produce serious disorders of perception and judgment.

Tranquilizers were thought to be nonaddicting. However, the meprobamate group has been shown to be addicting if taken in fairly large amounts over a period of months.[9]

[7] *Ibid.,* p. 19.
[8] Yost, *op. cit.,* p. 55.
[9] Yahraes, *op. cit.,* p. 20.

Physical Effects of Drugs

In general, narcotic drugs are classified as depressants (sedatives) or stimulants. The sedatives have a soothing, calming effect upon the nervous system. The stimulants, on the other hand, excite and keep the person awake.

The depressants. Morphine, codeine, and the synthetic narcotics are used medically to ease physical pain. The reader who has been treated for kidney pain, stones, migraine, or cancer may well have experienced the soothing relief afforded by these drugs. A person whose body is experiencing even the severest pain can remain reasonably comfortable while under the influence of a strong depressant.

A patient was admitted to the hospital with third-degree burns over seventy-five percent of his body. His raw, exposed flesh oozed body fluids for a period of several months. Finally, skin grafts were taken from the few unburned spots and placed on the more severely burned areas. During the entire period of hospitalization, the patient was sedated. Though his body must have been experiencing extreme pain, the patient was only aware of the discomfort of having to lie still. He talked coherently about himself and his situation and even responded humorously at times.

Within a few minutes after receiving such sedation in sufficient quantity, the face flushes, the pupils of the eyes constrict, there is a tingling feeling around the nose, the mouth, and the stomach. A calm passes over the consciousness. The painful areas become a throb, a murmur, then have no feeling at all. The patient is at ease and usually goes to sleep.

The depressant drugs' ability to relieve pain is not fully understood. It is known, however, that several mechanisms are involved: (1) The threshold for pain perception is elevated by depressing the cerebral cortex. (2) As the cortex becomes depressed, the threshold for perception of pain is raised. This is an important factor, due to anxiety associated with pain. As anxiety is relieved, there is less threat of pain, so (in actuality) less pain. (3) As has been previously indicated, depressants contain strong sleep-inducing properties—and sleep in itself raises the threshold for pain by approximately 50 percent. (4) Most depressants have a strong euphoric-producing property. When the self-critical faculties become inhibited, the individual is less aware of his situation and, though his pain may still persist, he may not be concerned about it.[10]

Drugs administered under medical supervision are a blessing to man. Drug addiction is harmful. There is little evidence to show harmful effects of drugs upon the body organs, but the continued use of depressing or stimulating drugs upsets the normal performance of the vital parts of the body.

For example, an undernourished condition may result because a person on drugs loses his appetite and does not eat properly. Depressants may cause constipation. While narcoticized, the person feels no pain. He may actually become sick and die without realizing the significance of his illness. While experiencing the euphoric state mentioned earlier, the addict detaches himself from many normal concerns and neglects medical and dental checkups that would ordinarily prevent serious illness.

Addicts are not careful in administering the drug to themselves. Unsterile conditions occasionally result in blood poisoning, jaundice, and other blood diseases being passed from one addict to another through the use of an infected hypodermic needle. As a more indirect effect of drugs, the addict may fall and hurt himself while in a stupor or may fall asleep in bed with a lighted cigarette in his hand.

The burned patient referred to earlier had been an addict for many years. And inadequate person to begin with, his motive in life was to get drugs from day to day. He was involved in an accident that resulted in a broken leg for him. This meant he had a valid excuse for receiving drugs (to relieve the pain of the break in his leg). Several weeks after the break, he was still calling for heavy sedation and was getting it. One day, while the family was away from the house for a few minutes, he helped himself to the pills, which were close by the bed. A few minutes later, while smoking a cigarette, he passed out cold, the bed caught fire, and he would have been burned to death had not someone run into the house and pulled him out.

Perhaps the greatest danger of drug addiction is the fatal "overdose." This may occur after the addict has been completely with-

[10] Ausubel, op. cit., p. 19.

drawn for awhile. In his eagerness, he may miscalculate and take more of a given drug than is necessary to sustain him—this may result in death. The possibility of overdose is risked when the addict buys drugs on the illegal market, because he does not know the exact strength of the drug he is buying. The cost is usually an indication of the strength. By the time heroin gets to the user it is mostly milk sugar, but it does happen that an addict gets hold of significantly stronger drugs than he is used to taking. When he does, the result is sudden death.

The abstinence syndrome is one of the most dreaded experiences for the addict. This occurs when the addicting drug is not taken after a sustained period of regular usage. The addict first begins to worry about becoming sick. The anxiety produced by the worrying makes him frightened and uncomfortable even before he actually becomes sick. The onset of illness is about four to twelve hours after abrupt withdrawal, depending upon the drug used, and is marked by sweating, running nose, chills, and gooseflesh. He becomes nauseated and has severe cramps in his stomach. He just feels wretched. As one addict put it, "I felt so bad, I was mad that I couldn't die." Reaching a peak in about forty-eight to seventy-two hours, the sickness then begins to subside, and within five or six days the major symptoms have abated.

The stimulants. Cocaine and the amphetamine drugs, though psychologically addicting, do not develop physical tolerance and hence no true withdrawal symptoms occur. Taken generally for their euphoric properties, they generate feelings of elation, superiority, and relief of fatigue. While intoxicated, the person may see weird visions, experience paranoid delusions, become aggressive, or even assaultive. While under stimulation, the person feels no fatigue and can literally wear himself out.[11]

Effect of Drugs Upon the Emotions

Generally speaking, the effect of drugs upon the emotions depends upon the individual and why he uses them. For most people, a single or several doses of drugs are really of little consequence, and one cannot reasonably assume that with one such experience a person's

[11] *Ibid.*, p. 110.

life is changed to any consequential degree. Many persons are on drugs for months at a time, under strict medical supervision, and are taken off the drug with little or no withdrawal symptoms, and no effect upon the emotions. In fact, this person is usually glad to be able to get along without having to take the drug at all.[12]

The person who develops a strong craving for the drugs after a few doses must have some prior need that the drug fulfills. For example, drugs relieve anxiety related to several things:

Aggression is reduced through use of some narcotic drugs. Numerous persons who become addicted have outwardly been rather passive in nature, while underneath they were very aggressive. Not being able to compete, they tried to avoid competitive situations that might provoke them. As a result, all their aggression was turned inside themselves. When they discovered drugs they found that their anxiety was relieved and they didn't care anymore. Drugs do not resolve the conflicts; they only ease the pain for a time. Even at that, the addict knows it is still there.

Sexual expression is another source of anxiety the addict attempts to resolve by using drugs. Opiate drugs reduce sexual urges. Women who are strongly addicted to opiates will stop menstruating. Persons heavily addicted may experience a reduction in sexual drive. Addicts will frequently unrealistically brag about their numerous conquests and list all the women who are just crazy about them, but usually this is all in their minds. They boast of their sexual powers to keep up an image for themselves and others. If they had no serious problems in sexual identification, they would be able to stay with a partner and enjoy the relationship. One addict stated: "I made it just fine so long as I played the field, but when I settled down with this one broad [woman] I began to chip [use a little bit of drugs off and on] and before I knew it I was hooked [addicted] and just couldn't stop."

Inadequacy, too, is a problem the addict tries to combat by using drugs. Many people with above-average intelligence still feel that they are inadequate to meet problems of living. Under the influence of drugs they find that they just don't care anymore whether they measure up or not.

[12] *Ibid.*, p. 37.

Depression is another feeling common to most addicts. It is a feeling the addict may experience after thinking of himself in low esteem. This idea of himself may be the result of continued rejection. Many case histories of addicts reveal a story of a person having been passed from one relative to another, eventually to be turned out into the street. He had no one to whom he felt he could belong. Rather than face this thought he began to cover up the feeling. He discovered that in many ways it was safer (psychologically) to take the relief offered in drugs than to run the risk of being rejected again.

I hope no doubt is left in the mind of the reader as to whether drugs actually resolve any emotional problems, for they do not. When addicts in counseling sessions begin to be really honest about themselves and their feelings, they admit that even while heavily addicted they were not able to shake off the undesirable emotions that were problems for them. As one addict said: "When I was all strung out [heavily addicted] I was so busy trying to get the next fix [dose of narcotic drugs] that I didn't have time to even think, let alone be concerned about my real problems, but they were there all along. I guess I knew about them but didn't want to think about them. I still have them now, but at least now I can talk about them."

CHAPTER TWO

ACQUIRING The HABIT

Anyone who takes sufficient narcotic drugs daily for two weeks will become physically addicted and will experience the abstinence syndrome if the drug is discontinued abruptly. Most persons, however, will show little, if any, emotional upset. They will probably be happy to be well enough to do without medication. After taking drugs some people experience headaches and nausea that can be almost as uncomfortable as the malady for which drugs were prescribed. Others simply do not like the groggy feeling they experience while on drugs. They want to have full awareness all of the time, and they lose this control while on drugs. The many thousands of persons who have passed through our two large Federal narcotic hospitals in the last thirty years, however, indicate that a large number of people do become addicted. The question we must raise is: "What are the predisposing causes of addiction?"

Studies of addicted persons admitted to the Federal narcotic hospitals indicate that most addicts have mental or emotional disorders. A few are found to be neurotic, and a few, psychotic. Most fall in the sociopathic personality disorder category, a disorder formerly called psychopathic personality.

In general, persons take narcotic drugs to the point of addiction to relieve physical pain or emotional distress. Most persons take the drugs to relieve emotional distress. The distress may be felt as anxiety, tension, depression, loneliness, futility, or boredom. A significant proportion of persons take drugs to handle or to control intense feelings of anger. Unable to express the anger in a manner acceptable to society or himself, the person finds that drugs reduce his concern about the anger.

Borderline psychotic persons may take drugs to relieve feelings of dissociation. Dissociation means the person feels that he is crumbling and needs something to help him hold himself together. A closer look at most addicts, regardless of personality classifications, indicates that they have anxiety related to sexual identification and aggression. A study of case material suggests causes for these conflicts.

As with most chronic mental emotional disorders, the trouble seems to begin with early adverse life experiences of the person. The life experiences of addicted persons almost inevitably reveal family disruption—physical, psychological, or both. Some addicts' fathers left home when they discovered their wives to be pregnant. Some stayed, but the emotional strain between the two parents was so great that the child might have been better off to have had only one reasonably strong parent.

Most addicts who come to the hospital come from disorganized, uneducated Negro and Latin-American families. The family disruption of our Negro and Latin-American addicts has a frequently observed pattern.

The father is unstable, often weak and inconsistent, and may have been an alcoholic or an addict himself. He may have traveled a lot and was not home much of the time. He may have abandoned the family, leaving the wife to take full responsibility for the children.

The mother of the addict usually is overindulgent and rejecting in an inconsistent sort of way. Sometimes mothers have been too disturbed to care for the child, and we find that the child was reared by a grandmother, an aunt, or possibly a cousin. The person rearing the child is often psychologically deprived and turns to the child for affection. The child, even at a very early age learned that "Mom" and other adults in his environment had needs that he recognized as weak spots. He would play upon these weaknesses to get his own wishes. Through this process of manipulation he was able to get many of the things he wanted but was denied what he really needed, that is, mature, consistent, and stable parental authority. Instead, the strongest person he knew was a frustrated and inconsistent person who could not say "No."

For many, actual addiction begins during adolescence, when they have to make some decisions about themselves in terms of their own identity. It is the lack of a good relationship with parental figures that predisposes the addict to poor relationships with everyone later on. He has experienced a relationship only with parents who were often passive, frustrated, and inconsistent.

The male addict will tend to feel more comfortable with older women, whom he will manipulate and use for his own gratifications. If, perchance, he has children, he will find the competition with them for affection of the wife most difficult to tolerate.

Many addicts display passivity in their actions and relations with other people. The same situation that causes the sexual difficulties also precipitates these nonaggressive characteristics. Seldom straightforward in seeking to relieve his wants, he moves around the issues and manipulates them in the same manner as he did his parental figures to get what he wanted. His anxiety over being unwanted lowers his tolerance for frustration, and he will feel that he must always have immediate gratification.

The addiction-prone neurotic person is looking for something to relieve his anxiety.[1] He would like to have something change him in such a way as to compensate for his inadequate feelings and his depression over being rejected. When he takes drugs he doesn't feel so bad. He still has the same problems, but under the influence of drugs, he doesn't care so much.

Anxiety alone does not cause a person to become addicted. If it did, we would be unable to deal with the addiction problem at all, for man seems to be possessed with so much anxiety about so many things. Two other conditions are required for a person to become addicted. First, he must be introduced to drugs. Second, he must have a personal attitude that permits him to use a socially disapproved method of relieving distress.

There are at least three ways a person becomes acquainted with drugs. These shall be discussed under the following headings: Accidental, Deliberate, and Experimental.

Accidental

Some persons become addicted accidentally. This means the person is given the drug for the relief of physical pain in connection with some serious disorder such as kidney pain, cancer, back trouble, arthritis, and so forth. The drug dulls the person's response to the pain. If the person has underlying anxiety or depression it will relieve that, too. Under the influence of drugs, the person actually feels

[1] In contrast to sociopathic personality types looking for euphoria, or a "thrill," not relief from anxiety.

better than he ever has before, in spite of his physical problem. His physical pain is minimized by the drugs. His emotional pain is also reduced. He therefore feels comfortable. After a time he is taken off the drug. Though his physical pain will have subsided, the emotional pain seems to become more intense. Since he doesn't understand his emotional pain, he will attribute the troubled feeling to the physical malady and will call for more drugs to make him comfortable again. If drugs are denied him, he may do something drastic rather than work through his emotional difficulties and face himself.

The burned patient previously mentioned was in the hospital several months. During the entire time he was given sedation to ease his pain. After much skin grafting, his severe pain should have been reduced; his medication was therefore stopped. Although a group of specialists believed that it was time to take him off the drug, he began to call for medication. He had little physical pain but was emotionally miserable. Instead of going through withdrawal and getting off drugs, he checked out of the hospital against medical advice.

Another illustration of a person becoming addicted accidentally was a man who had gone into the ministry in his thirties. He served several years as an associate pastor and, according to him, had done very well. It was evident, though not to him, that his heart was not set on being in the ministry. For example, he continued to smoke cigarettes, contrary to his denomination's practice. He was not able to submit himself fully to the duties of ministering to people and needed to be pushed occasionally by the pastor-in-charge to do necessary things, that is, visit the hospitals, members, and prospective members. After several years, he took a small church of his own and, though he had achieved a position of being on his own (which he thought he wanted), was not successful. He could not lead his people in the way he wanted them to go. He would fret over their unwillingness to cooperate with him. He developed an ulcer. For him, the ulcer represented a status symbol. He attributed its development to hard work and a stubborn congregation. He was given medication (narcotic drugs) for the pain. The drug relieved the pain, and it also eased his mental pain. He found comfort in it. While he was enjoying this comfort, his church began to deteriorate. The more it failed, the more trouble he had with his ulcer, and the more medication was needed to soothe the ulcer. His wife, who had been very patient with him, finally left him because she had tired of his self-centeredness and of his habit of blaming others for his failure. This was the crowning blow. He saw that all was lost. He blamed the situation upon his physical condition, which he thought was precipitated by stubborn and hardhearted members of his church. He took an over-dose of drugs and almost died before he could be taken to the hospital.

In summary, the person who becomes addicted "accidentally" has a physical problem for which drugs are prescribed by a physician. The drugs relieve the pain. They also relieve underlying anxiety or depression. The person likes the relief from these emotional conflicts. After his physical pain has subsided, he will continue to have symptoms in order that he can continue to receive medication.

Deliberate

Another group of persons who becomes addicted uses the drug deliberately at first. Initially aware of the pain-relieving or stimulating powers of drugs, they take them for that reason. In this group are found physicians, nurses, and other persons who have a prior knowledge of the effect of drugs.

One physician was starting a new practice. He was working long hours trying to establish a reputation for himself. Before long, he became fatigued, but having the strong need to prove himself (which may have been anxiety due to lack of self-confidence), he began to take stimulants to keep going. Through continued use, he became so stimulated he could not rest. To rest, he began to take depressant drugs, thinking they would bring him back down to normal. He seldom could make the combination just right. He would get too much depressant and soon would have to take a stimulant, then more depressant, then more stimulant. The pressure of trying to keep a balance between his drugs took so much energy and produced so much anxiety that he began to slip in his practice of medicine. As this failed, he would increase his medication. Eventually he became completely frustrated, was unable to continue, and required hospital-ization.

Consider another illustration.

A man had become addicted while serving as a medical corpsman in the Navy. He would get drunk on alcohol while on liberty, then would use drugs to enable him to function the next day. After a while, he gave up the alcohol and stayed with the drugs. He had ready access to the drug supply in the pharmacy. It was wartime, and a close check was not kept upon the drug supply. As with all addicts, it was difficult for him to maintain a level dosage. (The body keeps needing more and more drugs. The more drugs a person takes, the less able he is to function properly.) Eventually, this man was caught and dishonorably discharged from the Navy. In civilian life his habit continued, but he had lost his source of supply. He was forced to buy what he could from drugstores and steal whatever additional supply he needed to remain comfortable. He was ultimately arrested and sentenced by the court.

These people who become addicted do not actually set out to do so. They are simply looking for relief. They have a prior knowledge of the pain-relieving qualities of narcotic drugs. They also know the addictive properties of drugs but rationalize that they are strong enough mentally and emotionally to overcome the drugs' addictive powers. They do not see that it is their weakness that motivates them to take drugs in the first place; for all practical purposes they are hooked before they start.

One further comment might be made about this group. They have the highest percentage of rehabilitation. Members of this professional group—physicians, nurses, and so on—seem to be able to become aware of themselves and to draw upon inner strengths to overcome the habit. They have yet another factor in their favor. They have experienced a measure of success in life prior to becoming addicted and can draw upon this fact for strength when they pick up life again.

Experimental

The largest number of addicts come from yet another group. We shall call these the "experimenters." They are usually adolescents who are seeking a thrill or something to make them feel better. Some of these come from the so-called "good homes." Though they have money, they may lack the love and acceptance they need and may seek gratification in a bizarre manner. They rebel against parental authority, a reaction which in itself may be normal and healthy. Adolescents need to "cut the apron strings" and "try their wings." But some rebel because they do not get what they need from authority. They may receive money, clothes, cars, and so forth, but not affection. They often behave in such a way as to bring shame and dismay upon the family. It is their way of getting even. Naturally, the family rejects this sort of behavior and may punish, instead of help the child to work through the difficulty. The punishment is interpreted as rejection, meeting with more rebellion, which in turn brings more rejection and establishes a cycle. Since they can't get along with their families, they look elsewhere for acceptance. In the search they find others who are rejected and band together (misery loves company) to form a society of their own. Parental authority, the law, and the church are all rejected by this new society. Its members feel that they have been rejected, so they reject everybody else.

Usually someone in this group has had some experience with drugs, perhaps marihuana. The group smokes marihuana and enjoys the "high" (feeling of exhilaration) it affords. While high, its members seem to care less that they are in an unacceptable group— and may, in fact, come to think of themselves as a very special group that has become enlightened, that is "in the know" and ahead of the rest of society (the "squares"). Someone else comes along and introduces them to heroin. They try it and discover that the effect completely relieves all the anxiety they had and, indeed, they do feel better than they ever did before. While using heroin all their tension disappears. They become addicted to the feeling of euphoria as well as to the physical addicting properties of the drug. When they do not have the drug they experience all their old anxieties again, but in greater proportion. In addition, they learn that after one has been using drugs for a while and is suddenly cut off, he experiences a terrible sickness. When he is unable to get drugs this creates a feeling of panic within the person, so that he is really hooked three ways: (1) the need to have anxiety relieved, (2) the longing for the euphoric feeling drugs provide, and (3) the fear of abstinence syndrome (withdrawal sickness).

A man in his mid-twenties was confined for narcotic addiction. He was an only child born into an upper middle-class family. His father's responsible position in a manufacturing firm demanded that he be away from home much of the time. The mother was a housewife who, since they could afford the services of a maid, didn't have to perform the menial tasks. She spent most of her time taking care of her appearance and partying with other women in her social set. Though very active, she had an assortment of aches, pains, and uncomfortable conditions. She was often irritable while she was at home. When her husband came home the trouble seemed to get worse. She would nag and fuss. Quiet and unassuming, he would retire to his newspaper or business magazine. On numerous occasions when she felt angry with her husband, she would say to the son, "I hope that you don't grow up to be like your dad." The child developed the feeling that he was Mother's little man. He would do things to get her attention and praise, but she, wrapped up in herself, was never aware that the child was seeking praise. She would notice him only when he did something that displeased her. Then she would chide him, "You are going to be just like your father."

When the child grew to the size at which he was no longer fearful of physical punishment, he began to seek status outside the home. He deliberately visited neighborhoods far below his social status. He had a car—a status symbol in the poorer areas. He would load up the car with "characters" looking for transportation. They considered him as "all right" because he chauffeured them around. Several in the group smoked marihuana. He didn't even smoke cigarettes, but his inadequate feelings prompted him to try marihuana so that he wouldn't be labeled a square by the group. Embarrassed by his clumsiness at first, he worked hard and soon got the knack of inhaling, becoming as high as the rest of the group.

With his new-found status and the high feeling smoking marihuana made available to him, he became more aggressive at home. For a while he only changed clothes there. Later, he moved out and took an apartment in the other neighborhood among his new friends. He continued to go home regularly to demand money, and always get it. He gave up his apartment and moved in with a woman fifteen years his senior. He had been introduced to her by the group, several of whose members had lived with her for a while themselves. She used heroin. He was afraid when she invited him to take some, but again his inadequate feelings prompted him to show her he was a man, so he "fixed." It made him sick, but he experienced the euphoric effect. After a couple of weeks he was hooked. With both of them using heroin, money was needed. She made enough for both of them, at first, through prostitution. His part was to assist her in getting customers. Their habits grew and more money was needed, so he began to sell drugs whenever he could find a supply. He would buy what he could, cut it with milk sugar, and then sell it to other addicts. Occasionally, he would have to go to the Mexican border to obtain drugs, and this always presented the hazard of being caught at the border, which would mean going to prison. In spite of his precautions, this occurred when he was stopped one day as he re-entered the country. The agents went to the exact spot in the car where he had hidden the drugs. He was tried and sent to prison for five years.

We have referred to an addict who came from the right side of town. The majority of persons in this third group (the majority of addicts, for that matter) do not come from the better side. They are usually young people from the heavily populated, low economic, minority-centered areas of our larger cities. These areas seem to be hotbeds for the breeding of narcotic addiction. Many studies on the terrible housing conditions of these areas are available. Two or more families may live in a store front. They have limited skills, few job opportunities, and only the money that is given to them by the welfare agencies. Children in this environment, who for all practical purposes are literally raised in the streets, look for something to give them status and a sense of security. This they find in drugs. True, it is false security, but they rationalize that since no one seems to care about them, they should be able to take a little pleasure from life, and the thing that gives them the most pleasure is the euphoric feeling of drugs.

In our society, ease and comfort are highly advertised without pointing up the need for integrity and moral responsibility. The people in this deprived group seek a shortcut to success. They do not achieve real success, nor actually acquire all the glamorous things they hear about or see. They may get enough money through illegal means to buy a Cadillac and a two-hundred-dollar suit, but that's about all they achieve. They are not encouraged by parents or neighbors to go through the legitimate steps in acquiring these things.

They see crime glamourized on television and in the movies. They rationalize, "Why become a square and work and do without when one can be hep and have what he wants."

A Negro teen-ager, fourth child in a fatherless family of seven (the mother wasn't exactly sure who had fathered any of the children) lived in a poverty-stricken district of a large city. The mother collected a tidy sum from the welfare agency of the community (so much money for each child), but she used only a small portion for the upkeep of the children, who were under the supervision of her own half-blind and crippled mother. She spent the rest on liquor and expensive clothing for herself.

The boy's playmates had similar family conditions—some a little better, not many worse. Most of their time was spent playing in the crowded streets, running as a gang, and looking for excitement. They would gaze with awe at the few well-dressed "sharp characters" (neighbor boys who through illegal means had acquired enough money to buy fancy clothes). More aggressive than others in the gang, the Negro teen-ager would approach the sharp characters and make deals with them to peddle marihuana cigarettes to the others in the gang. This brought him high esteem, for he was now in business. The gang was introduced to heroin, and he was able to make a business venture out of that. He would get enough for himself and supply others who had money to buy it. He demanded cash for the drug, making it difficult for his customers because they had no cash. They had to resort to stealing to get cash, but in that neighborhood there was very little of value to be stolen. But addicts are persistent and will go to any lengths to get drugs, so his customers would eventually show up with the necessary money. Within a few months he was a "big man" in the neighborhood. He wore a flashy suit and expensive shoes. He thought of himself as the benevolent provider who takes care of his people's needs. One day one of his customers came up with a man and said that this man was a friend who was "sick" (addicted and needed drugs). The first reaction the provider had was to say "No," but the customer appealed to him and so did the friend. This appeal touched his need to be the "big man." He sold the stranger some heroin—the stranger turned out to be a Federal narcotic agent and made an arrest.

In summary, to become addicted to narcotic drugs, a person must have the physical pain or emotional distress that are the predisposing causes and that drugs relieve.

The person must be introduced to the use of drugs. He may be given drugs under medical supervision for relief of pain and become addicted accidentally. He may have a prior knowledge of the power of drugs, take them to stimulate himself or to ease emotional stress, and through their continued, deliberate use become addicted. But the large majority of addicts begin as experimenters looking for "kicks" and discover in heroin an instant solution to all their problems.

Finally, the addict's conscience must let him take drugs. He must be in an environment where drugs are available, and the environment must contribute to the perpetuation of drug use.

CHAPTER THREE

METHODS Of USING DRUGS

The act of administering narcotic drugs to oneself ("fixing") may be a very private matter. One addict said, "I guess it's all right to fix in a group. The first time I used it I was with somebody else, but eventually I only fixed by myself. Usually I fixed in the bathroom, though sometimes in the bedroom or the kitchen. Mostly in the bathroom though, and I would lock the bathroom door even when there was no one else in the house. Locking the door was added protection against anyone breaking in on me. And too, by being in the bathroom I could get rid of the stuff [drugs] if I had to." (If raided by the authorities he would flush the drugs down the commode.)

Amphetamines and Barbiturates

Tablets of amphetamines or benzedrine, called "pep pills" or "bennies," may be taken with water or alcohol, one or several at a time. Amphetamines generally are more readily available than morphine or heroin. Young people who are looking for kicks may obtain these drugs from a number of sources. The medicine cabinet in their homes may contain a prescription. Robbing drugstores is another source of drugs. Most of the amphetamines are purchased illegally from "pushers" (peddlers).

During the experimental period, young people take these tablets at parties to try to get high. They take the tablets with soft drinks or beer, if beer is available to them. The mixture of beer with tablets is supposed to give an extra kick. Generally speaking, the taking of amphetamines by teen-agers is a group action. The individual who may have difficulty functioning in groups discovers that he loses his inhibitions while on a high (on pills) and is no longer afraid to relate to others.

Pep pills are often taken as a part of group action, but barbiturates or "goof balls" are usually taken by the individual alone. Many adults take barbiturates to help them sleep. An emotionally upset person who finds it impossible to sleep may take barbiturates as a sedative. One addict stated:

"I only took medicine [barbiturates] so I could sleep. I had to have my rest at night in order to be able to work during the day. I would toss in bed, unable to sleep until about midnight. I would get up, take a couple of capsules, then fall off to sleep. Then I would wake up at 2:00 A.M. and be wide-awake. I would lie there a while, but finally to get to sleep, I would have to take two more capsules. These would put me to sleep, but I would wake up again about 4:00 A.M. Knowing that I didn't have to be at work until 9:00 A.M., which was still five hours away, and that I had only slept possibly three hours, I would take two more capsules. I would fall off to sleep, but this time I might not wake up until late in the afternoon."

Marihuana

Marihuana smoking may also be a group activity. The purpose in smoking marihuana is to reduce inhibitions and to create a feeling of exhilaration. While intoxicated, the person may feel that he is the life of the party. Repressed feelings are released. The person may become stimulated sexually and relate more aggressively. Others report that while smoking marihuana they had become more passive and felt depressed and subdued. Many patients have said that after continued use of marihuana the drug loses its exhilarating effect, and that after smoking, a person only experiences a depressed and let-down feeling.

One man explained his first experience with marihuana as follows:

"I had read about it [marihuana], heard others talk about it, but was afraid to try it myself. I had heard warnings not to smoke a cigarette that tasted sweet. I remember the subject was discussed in the hushed tones used when people talk about sex. Of course, this only enhanced my curiosity. I was about seventeen at the time. A friend told me that he knew where we could get some marihuana. Out of curiosity and looking for a thrill, I went with the friend to the home of a friend of his. We bought a couple of cigarettes and went back to my house. At that stage in my life I had to find out things for myself. We had the cigarettes, so we smoked them. We went into the bathroom to do it. There was a record player going in the next room. I was told to suck in a little air at the same time that I inhaled the smoke. It was a little difficult to do at first, but soon I caught on. Then I just faded out. I didn't fall down or anything. I guess I said it right, I just faded out. The next thing I knew I was in another room, looking in a mirror, and was feeling of my face. It felt different, more oily than I thought it should, so I just stood there stroking my face and experiencing this new awareness. Time had been distorted, because I didn't know how long I had been in front of the mirror. In fact, time did not seem to have any meaning at all, it was all so peculiar. I noticed my senses were sharper. The music coming from the record player sounded like music that I had never heard before, and I began to get tremendously hungry. I went into the kitchen. There were some brownies in a can. I took the lid off the can and began to eat the cookies. My buddy came into the room, and when we saw each other we just started laughing. Not over anything in particular, we just felt giddy and silly and knew that the other one felt the same way, so we just stood there laughing. After awhile the whole thing began to wear off and we were back to normal again."

Paregoric

Paregoric is an opium preparation used by addicts. Addicts who use it generally are thought of as being in the same category as the "winos" in alcoholic circles. Sometimes referred to as the poor man's drug, paregoric is used orally or hypodermically. Orally, it is swallowed (as is) from the bottle. Dosage may vary from two to six ounces, depending upon the availability of the drug and the size of the habit. Some addicts report a habit of up to eight or ten ounces per day.

The process of taking paregoric hypodermically is complicated. The solution must be reduced to opium. This is accomplished by boiling the solution until the alcohol and the camphor is evaporated and only the gums and opium are left. After this residue is filtered through cotton to absorb the gums, the opium is injected into the vein with whatever hypodermic apparatus is available.

In the words of an addict:

"Paregoric is a strange trip. It is difficult to get all the camphor out, so when it is shot into the vein you can feel the burn. It feels like a hot fire traveling through the blood. Then all of a sudden the pain that was running up and down the arm stops. I guess the opium had reached the brain. A warm glow sets in, a slow floating glow, and there's a warm feeling in the stomach, and everything's fine."

Heroin

Heroin is by far the most popular drug used by addicts. It is usually taken by one of two methods: sniffing up the nose or injection into the vein. Some of the older addicts still use the sniffing method. It is reported that many of the youngsters in the poor, depressed areas of the larger cities first start using heroin by sniffing. But the majority of addicts who use heroin take it intravenously. The powdery heroin is measured into a spoon—the same amount each time. Water is added, and a match is ignited and held under the spoon. This process is called "cooking." The purpose of cooking is to hasten the dissolving process and at the same time to warm the liquid. The warm solution is supposed to give a better feeling when injected into the vein. The dissolved, heated liquid is then pulled into a crude hypodermic apparatus, usually an eyedropper with a needle attached. As it is being drawn into the apparatus the solution is filtered through a small ball of cotton to strain out gums. The addict then puts a tourniquet above the vein to be injected, which is usually in the bend of the arm or the forearm. The tourniquet, often a belt, is held with the teeth. The tourniquet prevents the return flow of blood in the superficial veins so that the veins under the skin stand out prominently. Experienced addicts can inject themselves with either hand. When the vein is entered, a little blood is drawn out to mix with the heroin, and then the mixture is injected (see Figure 4). Sometimes, when an addict is not desperate for a fix, he may play before making the full injection. Playing is repeating the process of drawing a little blood and injecting a little of the solution several times before injecting the full amount. Some addicts have referred to this process as masturbating with heroin.

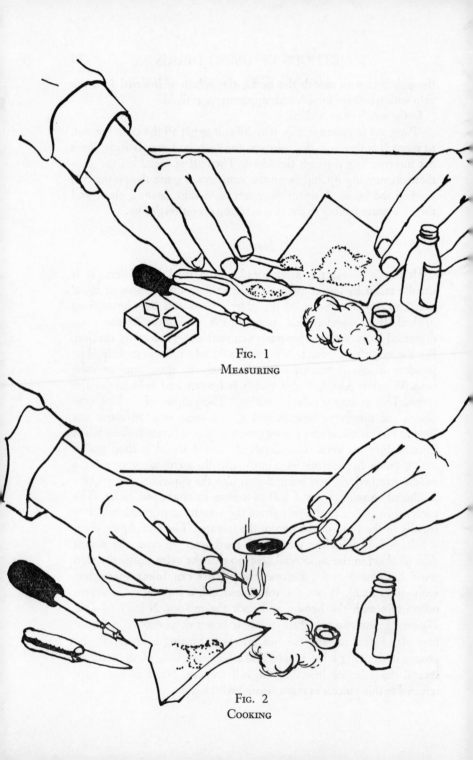

FIG. 1
MEASURING

FIG. 2
COOKING

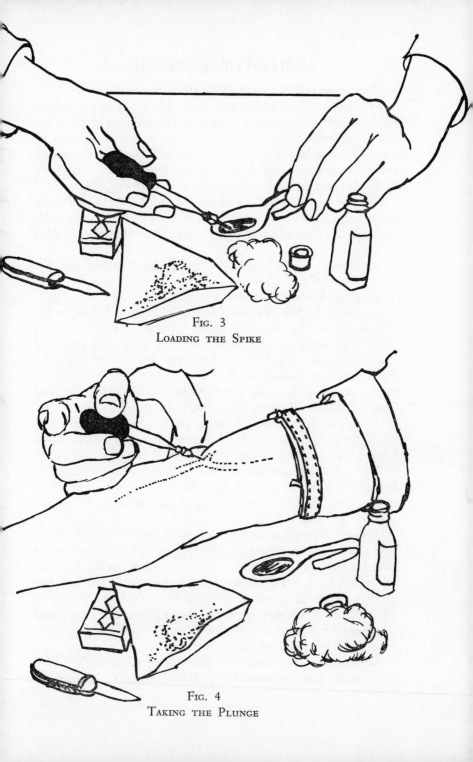

Fig. 3
Loading the Spike

Fig. 4
Taking the Plunge

There are several things to consider about the use of heroin.

The flash. Many addicts who use heroin report an unusual experience in the early stages of addiction. The sensation is called "the flash." Felt immediately after the injection, the flash is described by many addicts as "floating on a cloud." Actually, the heroin causes an autonomic nervous system reaction which, because it manifests itself in the abdomen, is sometimes described as an "abdominal orgasm."

This experience is so delightful that the addict seeks to achieve the feeling each time he fixes. However, it is reported that as a habit builds up, the flashes become more infrequent, until eventually there are none.

"The first few times I used I got terribly sick, but there were the few moments of flash so it was worth it. For the flash is the thing. You don't get it when you sniff or take pills."

The nod. A few minutes after the injection of heroin, as the drug begins to take effect, the addict becomes drowsy and sleepy. There is a mixture of comfort and discomfort. He may be nauseated and his stomach will feel fluttery, but at the same time he will feel a warm glow, first in his stomach, then all over. There is usually an itching sensation about the face, and he will sit and scratch and "nod" (drowsiness almost to the point of unconsciousness.)

"It was nice to sit and nod. I used to listen to soft music and sip on something cool and sweet. My stomach was upset, so the cool liquid felt good. Ice water had a soothing effect, milk was good, too. I liked milk best, but it seemed to cut the high, and the experience didn't last as long. Just to sit and nod, that's the way to live. I felt sufficient unto myself. Nothing seemed to be of any consequence, all my troubles were dissolved."

During this period an addict's difficulties do seem to fade out, at least as far as he is concerned. The nagging wife, the confronting boss, his debts, all his anxieties—everything that troubles him—are minimized. He is still conscious of all these problems, but for a few minutes they are at such a distance that they do not seem important. Of course, we know that, often, the longer problems are postponed the more they are compounded, but when fixed the addict either is not aware of this or doesn't seem to care.

The needle. The needle may mean many things to the addict, but primarily it means instant health. It means instant relief from the terrible anxiety he feels when he needs a fix. Addicts say that as soon as the needle enters the vein that they begin to feel relieved and that within a matter of minutes they experience an itching about the face and a warmness in the stomach. Calmness envelops them, and all symptoms of the abstinence syndrome disappear.

The effect of the needle is not to be minimized, because there have been instances in which an addict suffering from abstinence syndrome has been given an injection consisting of water containing a very small amount of narcotic—with the result that his symptoms cleared up for a short period of time and he was comfortable.

"There's something about that needle. I used to think how crude to be sticking needles in your arm, and the first few times, I must admit, I was scared, but the good feeling I got afterward was much stronger than the discomfort. After awhile, when I got hooked, I guess I came to worship the needle. Oh, not the needle, really it was the heroin, but the needle was the way I got to it, or rather it got to me, and the trip was instantaneous."

Another patient stated: "I can remember being, oh so sick. I was having the shakes and cold chills. I felt deathly ill. It seemed like I was being torn apart and at the same time the whole world was crushing in on me. Then, just a little powder, and when the needle went in 'boom'—well again, just like that."

Morphine and Liquid Synthetics

Morphine is usually obtained in the form of a small white tablet. The tablet is dissolved in a small amount of water in a hypodermic syringe and is administered hypodermically. Morphine and liquid synthetics are injected into the arms or into the legs. Sometimes the injection is made directly into a vein in order to achieve a quicker reaction.

It is not uncommon to see an addict who has, after administering these drugs to himself for some time, developed large ulcers on his arms and legs. The sores are caused by failure to employ sterile precautions when administering the drugs. Addicts will use dirty needles. Nor are they particular about the environment in which they use the drug. Sometimes they will take their injections in the most unusual surroundings.

"I had been riding on the bus for a couple of hours. I was on my way across the state because I was just too hot in the place where I lived. The police kept me under constant surveillance or at least it seemed to me that they did. I thought if I visited this friend in the other part of the state I could find refuge for a little while at least. I had enough heroin in my pocket for one fix. I was hoping to be able to last until I arrived at my destination before fixing. That way I would be in shape to last until I could find a supply in the new town.

"The trip took longer than I thought. The bus was hot and it rolled and pitched as we rode along. I began to get sick. When I felt the sickness coming on I tried thinking about something else. I looked out of the window of the bus and tried to concentrate on the scenery. I counted telephone poles, but the monotony of counting only added to my sickness. The towns we were passing through were only hamlets. Whenever the bus stopped it was just beside the road to pick up one lone passenger and this only took a couple of minutes.

"It seemed like an eternity before we pulled up in front of a large service station with a cafe attached to one end and the driver shouted, 'Rest stop—twenty minutes.' It was like someone called my name. I shot out of the seat and literally ran over people as I tried to get off that bus. As I brushed past people in the aisle of the bus I remember them saying, 'Well, of all the nerve!' It wasn't nerve, hell—I was sick.

"I ran for the rest room. It was an add-on room to the cafe, with one lavatory, one urinal, and one stall. I ran for the stall. On the bus I had dreamed of the privacy of a stall. I panicked when I saw there was no latch on the stall door. I had no other alternative. I had to fix. I threw my jacket over the door hoping it would say 'Occupied' for me. Men started coming in the little room. I could tell there were already five or six and there was really just room for three. They would bump up against the stall door. Then one would try to open the door. I tried to hold the door closed with my foot while I got out my kit. I was so nervous I dropped the spoon in the commode. It really didn't matter since I had to use commode water to cook with anyway. I got ready and sat down. Then I couldn't find a vein. Seemed like everything was going wrong. I hadn't had time to do the cotton bit, I couldn't find a vein, and those bastards were banging on the door. I finally made it. It didn't take long before I began to feel better. I put up my kit, flushed the commode, and walked out of the stall like I owned the place, completely aloof to the stares I got from the other men. I had mine. They'd have to get theirs the best way they could."

CHAPTER FOUR

DESIGN For PROCUREMENT

Drug addiction doesn't actually happen accidentally. The person who becomes addicted must have some predisposing characteristics in his personality. These may include feelings of anxiety and depression due to unhealthy early environmental experiences. The person must also find relief from these symptoms in drugs. The person must possess a flexible conscience that will allow him to take illegal drugs for relief of his symptoms. He must be introduced to drugs, and finally, he must be in an environment where drugs are available. Without drugs the person is only addiction prone.

Once addicted, the procuring of drugs becomes all-important. All the anxiety and frustration in connection with the person's self-identity and his ability to live and function comfortably and effectively are transferred to the procuring of drugs. He becomes less concerned with himself, his family, and his work; he thinks only of how he can manage to get drugs. Bills piling up no longer matter. Tension in the family is no longer any concern. The loss of job or friends or prestige or anything else is of no consequence to the addicted person. The only thing that really matters is getting drugs.

At first it doesn't take much of a drug to satisfy his needs. As he continues to use, it takes more and more drugs to do the same thing. Eventually, getting enough drugs to maintain some sort of a balance becomes the major problem in the life of the addict.

While in the chipping stage, even though he isn't using much, the addict begins to think about tomorrow and whether or not he will be able to get drugs. But when he gets really hooked, it's no longer a matter of tomorrow, it is "Where and how am I going to get the next fix?"

Where and how to get the next fix is a part of the immediate problem every addict faces.

Legal Factors

Strict rules govern the manufacturing and distributing of narcotic drugs.

Prior to 1914, anyone could walk into the corner drugstore and purchase any narcotic drug on the market. In addition, many of the patent medicines contained large amounts of narcotics. The result of this laxness was an estimated 150,000 to 200,000 people addicted to drugs.[1] Many were not aware that they were addicted. They only knew they needed more and more of the medicine they were taking in order to keep going.

In 1914 the Harrison Narcotic Act was passed. This act had several provisions. It placed a graduated tax on the production and sale of narcotic drugs. It limited the amount of narcotic drugs that could be contained in a medical preparation available to the public without a doctor's prescription. It set up the mechanics for stringent record-keeping on the manufacturing of narcotics and their distribution. This meant that drugstores, hospitals, and physicians were required to order their drugs on special forms provided by the Internal Revenue Service. Physicians were, and still are, required to keep a record of the amount of drugs dispensed, the date, the name and address of the patient for whom the drug was prescribed. The act provided penalties for persons convicted of violation of any part of the act.

The purpose of the act was to direct the manufacture and distribution of narcotic drugs through medical channels to consumption use for medical or scientific purposes only.

It has become necessary for the addict either to go to a physician for his drug (and the physician is in no position to give the drug haphazardly, either legally or ethically) or to turn to illegal means. Since most addicts have no actual physical condition for which drugs may be legally prescribed, they turn to illegal sources for their supply.

Essentially, the habitual use of narcotic drugs without valid medical reason becomes illegal. In this respect there is a big difference between addiction to drugs and addiction to alcohol. The person addicted to alcohol can go into any liquor store and purchase alcohol,

[1] Harry J. Anslinger and Wm. F. Tompkins, *The Traffic in Narcotics* (New York: Funk & Wagnalls Co., 1953), p. 257.

provided he is of age. He can consume the alcohol until he kills himself if he so desires. Until he becomes abusive and destructive of other people or their property, he has not violated the law. It is interesting that we as a society can be so rigid and strict in some areas and yet so lax in others.

Since Federal and state laws restrict the sale and distribution of narcotic drugs, the addict violates the law when he procures the drug. Being addicted in itself is not a Federal offense. Possessing narcotics without a valid prescription is illegal. Possession of marihuana or heroin is illegal, because they are not recognized as medical therapies.

Expense

Narcotic drugs purchased through legal channels are relatively inexpensive when compared with other pharmaceutical preparations. The addict is seldom able, however, to purchase drugs through legal channels. He must turn to illegal sources. When the peddler risks a minimum of five years in the penitentiary every time he makes a sale, it is understandable that the price asked for illegal drugs will be substantially increased.

Amphetamine and barbiturate tablets purchased illegally may cost from twenty-five cents to fifty cents each, depending upon the seller and how much the buyer is willing to pay. Marihuana cigarettes may cost from fifty cents to one dollar, again depending upon the seller and ability of the buyer to pay.

Heroin, the most popular drug among addicts, is no doubt the most expensive as well as the most difficult to obtain. Illegal in this country, heroin must be smuggled in, and the risk of being apprehended that the smuggler takes doubles the original value of the drug. Once in the country, the pure heroin is usually the property of the powerful crime syndicates. They distribute the drug to wholesalers (usually persons within the organization), who cut the drug. "Cutting" means to mix the heroin with equal parts of milk sugar. This doubles the amount of substance the wholesaler has in his possession. He then distributes the drugs, which again are cut to double the money and then sold to the person who will eventually get the drug to the addict. Of course, the pushers cut the substance again with milk sugar, in order to double their profits, so that the addict who makes the purchase actually gets more milk sugar than heroin. Dealers may add other substances to the heroin-milk sugar mixture. Aspirin, barbiturates, or anything else they can get is added to give a kick. When purchasing heroin, the addict may want to put a little of the mixture on his tongue. This is called "tasting." The purpose of tasting is to try to determine the ratio of heroin to milk sugar. Heroin has a bitter taste, and the sugar is sweet. To fool the addict, the seller may add quinine to the mixture. The quinine may fool the addict, but it has a harmful effect upon his veins. There are usually so many additions in the mixture that the addict doesn't really know what he is getting. Appropriately, the mixture is often referred to as "shit" among addicts. "Good stuff" is the term the addict uses when speaking of a mixture with a high ratio of heroin. By the time the user gets the mixture it will only contain 2 to 6 percent heroin.

Heroin is sold in capsules, in little plastic sacks, or in folded pieces of paper. Common terms for these containers are "caps" or "papers." Each section of the country has its own terminology. The most frequently used term is "paper." The price of a piece of paper will depend upon the ratio of heroin to milk sugar, the total amount of substance in the paper, the attitude of the seller the day he makes the sale, and finally, the ability of the buyer to pay. A paper may cost from three to twenty-five dollars. To illustrate how much it costs the addict per day: A person who is heavily addicted and is used to getting a high percentage of heroin may use two or three three-dollar papers each time he fixes. He may have to fix at least four times a day. The reader will want to remember that when the addict is really hooked he will have to fix around the clock. His body does not take time out for a good night's sleep. Using six to nine dollars' worth of heroin four times a day means that the addict's habit costs from twenty-four to thirty-six dollars a day. Some will spend a little less than that amount, but many will use much more.

Procuring

Since drugs are illegal, how does the addict obtain them?

From the physician. Many addicts will try the legal channels first. They will go to a physician and complain of all manner of aches and pains. Perhaps the person has experienced a serious illness or injury for which drugs were prescribed. Maybe the person actually became addicted while taking drugs for a particular malady. He will complain of lingering pains and his inability to tolerate them. The addict usually is seeking to get a refillable prescription, but this is impossible because prescriptions calling for narcotic drugs must be verified by the prescribing physician at each filling. Some addicts who present themselves for treatment at our narcotic hospitals tell of physicians who, out of sympathy, kept them supplied with enough drugs to keep them comfortable. This does happen, but the occurrences are few. Generally, the addict who is experiencing the abstinence syndrome is reluctant to go to a physician for fear the latter will discover the lack of actual justification for drugs and will insist upon the addict being hospitalized and withdrawn from drugs. In addition, the addict is afraid the physician will report the visit to the narcotic authorities. In general, addicts do not visit physicians in order to get drugs unless they are reasonably sure that the physician will give them the drugs they seek or that at least, if he denies them the drug, he will not report their visit to the police.

"I went to a doctor's office and explained to him that I was a police detective. I had a badge which I had purchased at a pawn shop and I showed him that. I tried to be calm and at ease, which was very difficult to do since I needed the medicine so bad. I told the Doc that my partner and I had apprehended an addict and he was getting sick on us, and I wanted a prescription so that we could pick up some drugs at the drugstore down the street before we took him to the jail. He seemed to buy my story, at any rate, he took his pad and wrote out a prescription. I really couldn't tell whether he actually believed me, but I am always suspicious. I guess it is fear of being caught. Anyway, I took the prescription down the street to the drugstore and gave it to the druggist. It seemed like he took an awful long time to fill it. I began to get jittery. Then all of a sudden two real policemen and two detectives walked into the pharmacy and came straight back to the prescription bar where I was standing. They made the arrest. The doctor had called the police and told them what he had done, then he called the druggist to alert him and told him to stall me until the police got there, and he did, and here I am."

Drugstores.   If the addict cannot get the drugs from a physician, he will attempt to purchase something from the drugstore. He may appear at the pharmacy early in the morning or late in the evening and explain to the druggist that some friend of his is in severe pain and is in need of medicine to kill the pain. He may admit that the drug is for himself, but usually it is for somebody else. This is a way of trying to protect himself from being turned over to the authorities.

"I had a good thing going until I got caught, well until my druggist got caught. I used to get paregoric regularly at this little drugstore. That was before the rule was passed requiring a prescription (some states still only require signing a register to purchase paregoric). Even then you could only get an ounce or two at a time and were supposed to sign a book for it. This druggist was never inquisitive as to why I wanted the paregoric nor was he reluctant to give it to me any time I came in for it. Of course, I wasn't going to say anything if he didn't. Sometimes I used fictitious names because I knew the narcotic boys go around and look at the records from time to time, and I didn't want to have my real name showing up too often. One morning, when I got to the store it was closed. I waited awhile, then I began to get sick and just had to get something from somewhere, so I took out looking for another drugstore. I finally got a couple of ounces, which eased me a little, and I went back to my store. It was still closed. I discovered later from a fellow that the druggist was an addict himself. He had been messing with the records to cover up what he was taking, and the narcotic agent caught him."

For some addicts, procuring drugs is more complicated and time-consuming than just going down to the corner drugstore and picking up a couple of ounces of paregoric. Upon returning to the hospital for treatment of paregoric addiction, one man said:

"The drive was just getting too much for me. When I was young I could stand up to it, but now that I've turned sixty, I just can't get around like I used to."

The drive to which he referred was a round trip of two hundred and forty miles. He made the drive daily. He would stop at five little towns, and at each would make a purchase of paregoric. Since there were four or five drugstores in each town he would only be hitting a store once a week. He felt that a druggist would not get suspicious if he only came in once a week for an ounce or two of paregoric.

No distance is too great for an addict to travel to get drugs. Another addict related a story of driving almost one hundred miles each day to purchase, at small rural drugstores, a particular kind of cough medicine which contained a narcotic.

Stealing Drugs

Many addicts try to steal the drugs they need. They may burglarize a drugstore, taking money and drugs. Sometimes they will only take the drugs and not bother the cash register.

Other addicts may try to steal doctors' bags. These bags usually contain a pain-killer of some kind, and the addict is familiar with them all. The bags are stolen from parked cars, from offices, sometimes from nurses' stations in hospitals.

Some addicts who were experiencing severe abstinence syndrome have become so desperate for drugs that they have tried to steal drugs from hospital supply rooms.

If the addict cannot steal the drugs, he will try to steal the next best thing—a prescription pad.

"I had been trying to figure out for several days how I could get a prescription pad. I decided to steal one from a doctor's office. I went into an office that was full of people. I asked to see the doctor. I was told it would be some time before he could see me. I asked if I could use the rest room. I figured there would be one in one of the examining rooms. The receptionist said 'Yes' and told me to follow her. Sure enough, she led me to one of the examining rooms and pointed to a door. I thanked her and went through the door and waited for her to leave. When she went through the outer door I came back into the examining room and in a flash I was all over it. They say 'where there is the will there is a way,' and in a drawer underneath one of the tables there were a couple of pads. I only took one. I didn't want to be a hog, and I didn't want to raise any suspicions. When I got back to the lobby the receptionist was away from her station so I just walked right out the door."

The addict who is trying to steal anything will usually not resort to a face-to-face confrontation. He is very much afraid of being caught, and a confrontation or demanding drugs increases his chances of being caught. Being caught means going to jail, and going to jail means experiencing the abstinence syndrome without the benefit of drugs.

He will steal from parents or friends. He will pawn the television set, electrical appliances, or anything of value. He may write checks on the family bank account without any consideration of the needs of the other family members. Some will write "hot" checks, using fictitious names. Many are apprehended for writing hot checks or stealing money orders or postal checks.

Many addicts are good talkers and present a most convincing story. They call upon ministers, travelers' aids, various charity agencies, telling them of the most pathetic dilemmas. An addict in Texas told a minister that he had just heard that his little girl, who was living in New York with her mother, had just died. He wanted the minister to give him money to buy a bus ticket to attend the funeral. Of course he got the money. The addict had never been married.

Many addicts use different "con" techniques. One of the many that has come to my attention is that of the "furnace specialists." They offer to examine the furnace and certify its condition absolutely free. They tear down the furnace and report to the owner that there are so many things wrong that it is dangerous to use the furnace unless it is repaired. They present a list of needed repairs, and their bill. The bill is always payable in advance, to enable them to purchase the needed fixtures. If they get the money, they leave to get the fixtures but never return.

The heroin addict who comes from one of the underprivileged overpopulated, depressed areas of our large cities is generally uneducated and unskilled. He is usually unable to make a living wage, much less support a heroin habit which may cost twenty to thirty dollars per day. When he first starts using narcotics, he is usually still a teen-ager. At this point his formal education ceases, and he will probably not have the benefit of any type of job training. Too young to get a job at manual labor, uneducated and unskilled, the fledgling heroin addict is hard-pressed to support his habit. He frequently will resort to stealing as a means of making money.

Stealing in the underprivileged neighborhoods is a problem because there is usually very little to steal. No one in these areas has very much of value anyway, so there is little to be gained. The other recourse is to go to another part of town and steal from the large department stores. This, too, has its problems—only of a different nature. When the addict leaves his environment, he may be recognized by authorities as being out of his element. He is watched carefully by the police and is apprehended if he makes any suspicious moves. If he is successful in the stealing venture, he must then dispose of the stolen merchandise. He will sell the goods to a "fence" (buyer of stolen merchandise), who gives him only one-third the retail value, and sometimes less. If he needs thirty dollars for drugs, he must steal at least ninety dollars worth of merchandise. The addict knows it is impossible to continue stealing large amounts without eventually being caught. He knows that being caught means jail. Jail means being deprived of heroin and the subsequent discomfort of abstinence syndrome. The addict must therefore turn to other means of obtaining money.

Generally, his methods of making money are not too much out of line with what others in the neighborhood do to make money. In the depressed areas not everybody steals. But because so many do, those who don't frequently turn their heads or shut their eyes while stealing is going on. This behavior on the part of those who do not steal causes the observer to wonder whether or not stealing is actually unacceptable.

Another condoned activity in depressed areas is prostitution. The female addict may sell herself to make enough money to keep supplied with heroin. The male addict often may become a sort of friend to such a prostitute and procure for her. The female tries to make enough money to support both habits. Some male addicts live with prostitutes and may or may not assist her in her professional venture. If they do not assist in the procuring or do some sort of work themselves, it is difficult to say just what the male addict contributes to this sort of relationship. There are those who say that the male addict is very dependent upon women and, at the same time, hostile to them. In this sort of relationship, he would be completely dependent upon the woman for everything and, simultaneously, would be using her in a very degrading way. It is not infrequent that a male addict who is unable to make money enough to support his habit will force his wife or girl friend into prostitution. This act is called "turning her out."

Some addicts sell themselves to homosexuals. Many who do this take advantage of them. If robbed, the homosexual is unable to go to the police and report the crime.

Stealing and pimping usually are the methods used by addicts in the early stages of their addiction. As their habit grows, their need for more money increases. The addict turns eventually to selling. He is generally a very small dealer. His purpose is not to amass a fortune; he is only concerned with getting the next fix. The big dealers in narcotics usually are not willing to set up an addict in business, because their experience with addicts is disappointing. They know the addict is concerned only with himself and cannot be depended upon to take care of business. Therefore, the only time professional dealers will turn over heroin to an addict is when he has cash to purchase it. Since the addict has a constant need for drugs it follows that he is unable to save up enough money to make a big deal. He will only be able to buy a few small papers at a time. If he is lucky and is able to get some heroin that has not been cut excessively, he may divide the amount. Half he keeps for his own use. He will cut the other half with milk sugar and try to sell it to his friends for as much as he can possibly get. Of course, he will tell them that it is pure stuff. The buyer always knows it is not, but when the addict needs a fix, he will take what he can get.

Addicts who live in proximity to the Mexican border will go to Mexico to get their drugs. Heroin is also illegal in Mexico. The reason the addict goes to Mexico is that he can purchase heroin cheaper. He may find heroin that is stronger than that he could get in this country at the same prices. The addict who goes to Mexico will take a fix while he is there and then will try to bring whatever amount he has money to buy back into this country. He will try to hide the heroin in all manner of places on his person or in the automobile, but the inspectors at the border are so adept at spotting addicts and finding contraband that it almost seems as if they can smell it.

Stealing, pimping, selling, smuggling—any way to get drugs is acceptable to the addict. He stops short of using a gun. The use of a gun requires more aggression than most addicts can muster. He has no respect for the laws of society. Once addicted, he begins to think of society as that body which is determined to deprive him of his solution to pain and discomfort. In a sense he sets out to outmaneuver the law. If all the energy the addict exerts in his quest to obtain drugs were concentrated in another area, he could literally move a mountain. Procuring drugs requires not only all his energy; it requires all of his time. He gives himself completely to this task. To get his drugs, he will beg, borrow, and steal. No obstacle is too great if he thinks it will result in obtaining drugs. He pursues his goal, knowing that sooner or later he will be apprehended, yet on he goes until finally he forces the law to hold and restrict him by incarceration from the use of narcotic drugs.

CHAPTER FIVE

COMMON MISCONCEPTIONS

The minister as well as the general public has had to depend upon news and entertainment media for information about narcotic addiction. The information may be colorful and exciting or distasteful and depressing. But the portrayal of the addict and the problem of addiction has not always been accurate. The purpose of this chapter is to present some common misconceptions about addiction to assist the minister to understand the addict better and to supply the minister with information that he can impart to his congregation.

Addicts Appear Degenerate

It is difficult to determine what the general public thinks an addict should look like. Many are surprised when first they see one.

The author was to lecture to a group of visitors touring the hospital. Before he arrived his patient-assistant was serving as host to the group, answering their questions about the hospital. Later, during the lecture, one of the visitors asked, "When are we going to see an addict?" The visitor was surprised when told that he had already seen many and that their young host, who had made such a hit with them, was an addict. When asked what they had expected an addict to look like, no one was able to say. They just had not been prepared to see someone who looked and acted absolutely normal. One of the visitors said of the assistant, "I thought he was one of the staff."

Addicts are people; in many respects they are very particular people. Most addicts are very much concerned about the way they look and the way they dress. They like to wear expensive clothes and shiny shoes. Even in a hospital setting where everyone must wear uniform-type clothing, patients give extra attention to creases in their trousers and will spend hours polishing their shoes.

If there is one thing addicts can do well it is to make a good impression on people. They not only look nice, they talk nice and can show more manners than a butler. Of course, the addicts of whom I speak are those who have been free of narcotic drugs for a matter of weeks or months, but the same thing may be said of the person who is addicted. Many addicts report that even while using drugs they maintain concern for grooming and dress. It is only when the addict is experiencing abstinence syndrome and is unable to get the drugs he needs that he may neglect his appearance—and this is only a temporary situation. As soon as he is free of his sickness, either by getting completely free of the drug, or by using more drugs, he will revert to his habit of good grooming.

Many people visiting the hospital have expected to see a lot of old men. They, too, have been surprised at the age of the average addict. Twenty-five years ago the average age of addicts presenting themselves for treatment in our two Federal hospitals was in the late thirties. The average age now is in the mid-twenties.

The Terrible Withdrawal Sickness

The abstinence syndrome can be a most uncomfortable experience, but withdrawal from narcotic drugs can be accomplished with a minimum of discomfort within a hospital setting.

People who visit the withdrawal ward in the hospital are puzzled when they do not see disheveled people crawling under beds, flinging themselves against the walls, and screaming. They are pleasantly surprised to see people sitting around tables playing cards or checkers. Some are shooting pool. Some are watching television. Some are reading. Others are writing letters. A few are talking with nurses or nurses' aides. A few are asleep in their beds. Sometimes visitors do not believe that we have really shown them the withdrawal ward and will question the tour guide just before they leave the hospital, "When are we going to see patients being taken off drugs?" No doubt visitors expect to see in the hospital something similar to what they have seen in films or on television. Hospital withdrawal is just not that bad. This subject will be covered more fully in a later chapter.

Heroin Destroys Intellectual Capacities

Heroin does not directly cause any degeneration of intellectual functions.

"Drug addiction does not significantly impair intelligence or psychological efficiency. Drug addicts are able to work skillfully and efficiently if they want to, although speed may be reduced. Studies show a loss of speed in motor tasks, in verbal and motor reaction time, in verbal learning, and in computational work. It is highly doubtful, however, if this degree of impairment is of significant practical importance."[1]

Some addicts who come to the hospital for treatment are in professions requiring maximum use of the thinking processes and claim to have been able to function adequately during their addiction so long as they were able to get drugs required by their body. When asked what they meant by adequate, they were only able to say that their performance in several areas of living was satisfactory to themselves but was not necessarily satisfactory to others.

One addict said, "When I use drugs my family does not do without a thing, I work, I provide for my family." When he was questioned further, it was discovered that he gave money to his wife for support of the children only after he had purchased the drugs necessary to maintain his habit. His needs came first. When asked about this he said, "Well, I'm the one who makes the living, therefore, I should get what I need first so I am then able to make more money to take care of the others."

Many addicts have been asked, "If you were to wake up some morning and the family was without food, and the baby needed milk, and if you were beginning to experience withdrawal, what would you do?" Of all the addicts who were asked this question by the author, not a single one answered that he would get the milk for the baby. All said, "I would get my shot first then worry about the baby."

The very fact that a person uses drugs is an indication of the presence of serious emotional problems with which he is unable to cope

[1] Ausubel, *op. cit.*, p. 38.

in any other way. It is questionable whether such a person is capable of fulfilling the role of being a responsible member of a family and helping other members with their needs.

Some addicts say that while using narcotics they felt better and were able to do more than they had ever previously done. No doubt a person who is relatively free of tension and conflict is able to function better than a person who is not free. Narcotics do free people from tension and conflict. However, it is important to remember that if a person takes too much of a drug he will become drowsy and go to sleep. It is difficult to work while sleeping. Second, as a person continues to use drugs, his body builds up a tolerance which requires more and more drugs to do the same thing. If he does not get the added supply, he begins to experience withdrawal and becomes very uncomfortable. Maintaining a level dosage is difficult. If given a supply of drugs in advance, the addict is likely to use the entire supply at once.

A group of addicts were discussing the possible solutions to the drug problem. One suggested making drugs available to addicts. He went on to say this could be accomplished by giving the addict a prescription for a particular amount of drugs per week. This would keep him supplied and he would not have to resort to illegal means to obtain his drugs. Another addict said, "That would never work. If we were given a week's supply we couldn't discipline ourselves and make the stuff last for the week. We would end up shooting all of it in one day . . . then we would be right back out there looking for a connection." The group agreed that this latter analysis was probably true.

Addicts often say they make good adjustments if supplied with drugs. It has been my experience that drug users generally did not function prior to their addiction.

Addicts Entice Children to Take Drugs

It is difficult to determine where people get the notion that addicts stand on street corners close to schools and entice school children to start taking narcotics.

I was to speak to a men's group on the problems encountered in treating narcotic addiction. Before the lecture, an upset father commented, "I don't know what I would do to a fellow if he started my child to using drugs. . . ." I assured the father that it was not likely that anyone would introduce his child to drugs. I went on to point out the psychological and environmental prerequisites of addiction as well as the need for a supply of drugs, and that probably his child neither met the requirements nor had the supply. The father tried to believe me, but I wasn't sure that he had heard what I said.

Addicts are very careful about selling drugs. Contrary to the idea that they go around soliciting customers, addicts run customers off. They try very hard to sell only to personally known addicts, usually close friends, but even then they sometimes slip.

"This guy had fixed with me several times. Sometimes he had the stuff, sometimes I had it. I thought we were pretty tight [close friends]. I got hold of a good batch of stuff. He knew about it. He came over one day and wanted to buy some of it. I told him that I didn't want to sell any of it, but that I would give him a fix to make him feel better. He just insisted that I let him pay for some. I took his money, and when I did, a narcotics agent crawled through the window and arrested me."

Since being caught by narcotic agents in the act of selling drugs can mean five years in the penitentiary, the addict tries to be extremely careful. Usually he will only sell drugs to a known addict who has the money to pay the price he is asking for the drug. Schoolchildren rarely meet these requirements.

The Addict is a Sex Fiend

Addicts are not sex fiends. If anything, addicts tend to be passive and relate very poorly sexually. The history of many addicted persons coming to the hospital for treatment reveals that drug use began during the adolescent period. This is the time people begin to work through their sexual identification problems and begin to relate to the opposite sex. As was stressed in an earlier chapter, drugs reduce anxiety stemming from feelings of sexual inadequacies. Many use drugs to avoid relating to the opposite sex.

"I recall many times when I left the house to go see a girl friend. Usually on the way over to see her I would get to thinking about getting a fix. I wanted to feel more comfortable, and then I thought that when I fixed I could make a better impression, and make better conversation and would be a more interesting companion. When I got to thinking that way, before I knew it I was driving past the connection's house [a connection is a person who has a supply of drugs]. The next thing I knew I was fixed. I might eventually make it over to the girl's house in a couple of hours or more, but usually I wouldn't go at all. She would call the next day and really chew me out for not showing up or at least calling her and telling her that I couldn't make it. I lost more girl friends that way."

Usually male addicts would rather have a few male friends and drugs than make the effort to relate to girls. Many addicts have said that while on drugs they never gave girls a thought. Others say that during the time when they were heavily addicted all their sex drive was gone and they were unable to function sexually even if they had the opportunity. Generally, male addicts who live with women do so for reasons other than sex. It is not uncommon to find an addict living with a woman ten to fifteen years his senior. Some say that his reason for living with a woman older than himself is that it fulfills some sort of need to be mothered. In this sort of relationship the addict is usually simply living with the woman because she has some money that he can use to buy drugs. When all her money is gone he leaves, too, and takes up with some other woman who will supply him with money to buy drugs. Many addicts will live with a prostitute, but not for the purpose of sex. He is interested in her ability to make money, which he hopes she will give to him so that he can buy narcotics.

One of the questions sometimes put to addicts is, "If you had the choice between sex and drugs, which would you choose?" The following story will indicate the usual answer.

Upon release from an institution in which he had been incarcerated for several years, an addict was met at the gate by a beautiful woman. They went immediately to a hotel in which she had rented a room. The minute they got into the room the addict asked, "Where is the stuff?" She produced the drugs. He fixed. Passed out. A few weeks later he was arrested on a narcotic violation and sent once more to an institution, this time for a longer sentence. During his few weeks of freedom he had his drugs, but no sex.

Addicts use women, but when addicted they do not ordinarily use them sexually.

Addicts Are Violent

While in pursuit of drugs the addict may break into a drugstore, grab a doctor's bag, steal drugs from another addict, but as a general rule, addicts are not violent.

The stimulant drugs (amphetamines and cocaine) and marihuana distort perception and produce exhilaration, but seldom make a person violent, unless, of course, he is a violent sort of person to begin with. Most addicts are not.

The depressants (heroin, for example) reduce the activity of a person. After the addict has fixed, all he wants to do is to sit and scratch and enjoy the comforting drowsy experience he refers to as "being on the nod." After fixing, the addict is apt to stay as still as he possibly can so that the feeling will last. If he becomes active, the sleep-producing effect of the drug is reduced.

Narcotic drugs, then, do not provoke violence. A person may become frantic while experiencing abstinence syndrome, but as soon as he has a fix he will become calm and return to his usual passive self.

Of the many patients who come to the hospital for treatment, very few have a history of being assaultive or committing crimes of violence. Rarely is there mention of an addict using a gun. Usually, the crimes committed by addicts involve property, burglary, forgery, or writing hot checks.

Marihuana Is Addicting

Marihuana is not an addicting drug. It could be habit-forming in the same way as tobacco is, if someone were to smoke as much marihuana per day as he does tobacco. Usually a person will only smoke two or three marihuana cigarettes per day, whereas tobacco consumption may run as high as two packages (forty cigarettes) per day.

The danger in smoking marihuana is the distortion in sensory perception that it produces, not its addicting properties. A second factor is that marihuana is often a stepping-stone toward the use of heroin.

Addicts Should Be Punished

This concept is not acceptable to many nowadays. The majority of persons dealing with the problem of addiction feel that it is a sickness. They think that the addict is a very sick person and that punishment has no place in the treatment of sick people. In times past, the addict was considered an evil person who needed to be locked up in prison and left there.

Cure Requires Only Willpower

"The spirit is willing, but the flesh is weak" sums up the good intentions of many addicts. They have a dual problem. Addicted in body, they also lack the emotional maturity to decide against taking narcotics. However, the reader should understand that for an addict to say "No" to drugs requires much more than is required of an obese person who needs to push away from the table and a second piece of apple pie.

It must be remembered that drugs meet unconscious needs of the person. When these unconscious problems are being resolved or at least becoming less painful, then the person is dealing with more than just giving up some external habit. The heroin addict literally finds the "peace that passes all understanding." When he discovers ease and calm he is not likely to give it up without a struggle. Even though he resolves to stop using because of the trouble it causes with society, the law, and his family, he finds himself wandering back to take a fix. So many things remind him of the sensation. To the heroin addict, the striking of a match, the smell of sulphur burning, a spoon, hearing "jive talk," seeing a certain kind of walk, remind him of the feeling of heroin. With stress within, and so many symbols haunting him without, the addict has a real struggle in giving up drugs.

Addicts Are Never Cured

This is absurd. Addicts can be cured. Some addicts who have been treated for addiction have stayed drug-free for the rest of their lives. Many have been drug-free for five, ten, some for fifteen years. The question most people raise is, "What guarantee is there that an addict will never use drugs again?" There is no sure answer. However, just because we cannot guarantee that a person will remain drug-free is certainly no reason to assume that he will eventually take up the habit again.

One of the best analogies is to compare drug addiction with a common cold. Nearly everyone at one time or another has had a cold. Everyone who has had a cold has probably been cured. But who can guarantee that once free of the cold he will never have a cold again? Colds recur. Such is the case with addiction. A person may be free of drugs, but given the right set of circumstances and available drugs, he may slip. If a person slips, however, he can be treated again. If a person recovering from a cold has a relapse we do not write him off as a lost cause; we treat the person again.

A person's returning to drugs depends upon several variables: his ability to work, to gain employment, to sustain relationships with people who are stable drug-free individuals, his emotional status, and his desire to remain off drugs. Some of these factors are the responsibility of the addict himself. Other factors which influence him, for example, are community attitudes, family, job opportunities, and the like.

Summary

1. The addict is not necessarily degenerate in appearance.
2. Withdrawal can be accomplished with a minimum of discomfort in a hospital setting.
3. Heroin does not destroy the intellectual capacity.
4. Addicts do not entice children to use drugs.
5. The addict is not a sex fiend.
6. Addicts are seldom, if ever, violent.
7. Marihuana is not addicting.
8. Addicts should be treated, not punished.
9. Cure requires more than will power.
10. Addicts can be cured, and many are.

CHAPTER SIX

INITIAL PASTORAL CONTACT

No doubt the minister can help the addict, but as a general rule, addicts don't make a practice of calling on ministers. The author asked two hundred consecutive addicts admitted to the hospital if they had ever consulted a minister about their problem of addiction. Not a single one answered in the affirmative. This statistic may have real significance for us. Most of the addicts we treat at our hospital come from areas inadequately served by the Church. These areas are the heavily populated, economically poor neighborhoods of the larger cities. The patients who come to us from these areas have very little, if any, concept of religion, and in some instances their mode of living indicates a severe lack of moral values. Patients report that the Church is not a focal point of community life in these areas. They say that the only religious facility in most instances is the store-front variety of mission, which opens only in the evenings for evangelistic services. One reason for not one of the two hundred having visited a minister might have been that neither church nor minister was available.

Few ministers in the suburban churches will have occasion to counsel an addict. Although we have treated addicts at our hospital from all social levels and from many professions, upper- and middle-class persons infrequently come to us for treatment. It is generally from these groups that we find those persons who have had some religious training and may have counseled with a minister prior to their coming to the hospital. In some cases, it was the minister's insistence that led a patient to come to the hospital for treatment. In other instances, a relative of the addict went to the minister for advice, and the minister advised hospitalization. Some patients tell us that they did not see their own pastor but went to another. Others tell us they went to see several pastors. Some say they went to several pastors, but not for counseling.

This chapter is written for the pastor who may have an occasion to help an addict. It will be divided into three parts: (1) reasons addicts give for not consulting the minister, (2) things the minister should be aware of about the addict who comes to see him, and (3) specific things the minister can do for the addict.

To Call or Not to Call

To call or not to call is the question every counselee must answer when contemplating bringing some outsider into the private world of his problems. What can he expect of the outsider? If the counselor cannot help, will he hurt? Sometimes prospective counselees answer their own questions on the basis of misinformation or their own fears and suspicions. Unfortunately, some of their suspicions are well founded. What are some of these preconceived notions the addict has about what to expect from the minister?

I have asked many patients about their reluctance to consult the minister. Some of these patients have been well educated, reasonable, successful professional people. Some not only have claimed to be successful in their professional role but have maintained that they were respected and involved in the external workings of church programs, that is, they were on various boards and committees, or perhaps sang in a choir. I use the term *external* to differentiate between being involved in church activities and being involved in deepening their spiritual consciousness in relationship to God. In the more evangelical Churches, the latter process is termed *witnessing* or *soul-winning*. At any rate, I have known many addicts who had been active in the mechanics of their churches, but very few who had reached the point in their own religious experience where they felt comfortable in witnessing to others. Some of these patients who have had a relationship with the Church reflect some special areas of concern for us.

One patient had been a distinguished member of the same church for twenty-seven years prior to his admission to the hospital for treatment. When asked by a student chaplain if he had ever gone to his pastor with his problem, he said "No." Asked why, he related the following story:

"Over the years I've had many occasions to observe the pastor deal with people. Being around the hospital frequently myself, I have been with him many times in the sickroom. Quite frankly, and not meaning to be disrespectful, the pastor is like a cat on a hot tin roof when he is in the room with a sick person. It seems to me that facing sick people is almost more than he can bear. He looks out the window and says 'Hello.' Without looking at a person he jovially says, 'My you're looking good.' He then says 'Keep on getting better,' looks at this watch and says, 'Well, I've got a committee meeting that I just have to make. Sorry I have to rush like this,' and poof—he disappears! In the pulpit he is an entirely different person. Eloquent and poised, he has a command of the language and a flow of words with which he can sway and convince a vast congregation. On Sunday morning at preaching there is standing room only in a church that will hold over a thousand people. But when faced with an individual, he freezes up. I never went to him because I just plain felt that he wouldn't be able to listen to me and to understand."

I wouldn't judge a minister after hearing one person report his feelings about that minister. I am also aware that people can distort the truth to their own satisfaction, especially if it makes them appear in a better light. We pastors, however, need to become more aware of the image we present to people. In some instances, such as the case just cited, the pastor can shut the door to counseling before he ever gets started. The pastor mentioned here does not know of this particular problem.

Some patients have said that their reluctance to go to a minister about their problem of addiction was engendered by fears that he would judge and preach.

One addict said, "I went to several preachers, and with every one of them, it was the same old story, 'Son, how in the world did you ever get mixed up in such an evil thing? Don't you know it's wrong to defile the temple of God? Destroying your body like you are doing is a sin.' Of course I knew I was wrong. I felt bad before I went to the preacher. The reason I went to him was to find some answers, some solution, some help—certainly not a lecture that made me feel worse."

Though some ministers tend to be judgmental, it seems to me that some addicts are more judgmental of themselves. In most instances the addict feels bad about something, but the feeling need not be guilt. He could feel guilt, or it could be a mixture of guilt and resentment over not being able to get what he thinks he needs, namely, drugs to relieve his uncomfortable feelings. Many addicts feel intensely guilty for having lost control of themselves and resorted to drugs. Even if an addicted person has a prescription for drugs and a valid medical reason for using drugs, he will feel uncomfortable in telling people that he is addicted. The term *addicted* has a helpless, inadequate connotation to the addict, and to speak of himself in these terms is often more than the individual is able to do. Consequently, many addicts will not reveal their condition to anyone outside the immediate family, and they try to keep it from the family as long as possible. The following interview will illustrate how addicts attempt to conceal their problem.

CHAPLAIN: I see by your admission card that you belong to a church.
PATIENT: Yes.
CHAPLAIN: What sort of a member are you?
PATIENT: Oh, I attend regularly.
CHAPLAIN: Your minister knows about your addiction and your being here?
PATIENT: No.
CHAPLAIN: Why?
PATIENT: Several people knew that I had been having headaches and back trouble for some time. I decided that I would only tell people that I had to go to the hospital for awhile and not give any specific reason—and hope that they would assume that the hospitalization was for the headaches and back trouble.
CHAPLAIN: I can understand that you didn't want to publicize your problem, but why were you reluctant to confide in your pastor?
PATIENT: I suppose I was just ashamed. You see, I've tried to keep up a good image of myself and having to admit that I really wasn't what I have tried to make people think I was, was more than I could do.

The middle-class suburban pastor is not often likely to encounter persons addicted to heroin or morphine in his parish, but he will probably know of persons who attempt to relieve their unpleasant feelings with other drugs, that is, barbiturates and alcohol. Their inability to face their problems may be the same thing that makes them incapable of going to their minister with their problems. They may feel that as religious persons they should be able to rise above their problems. They take sedatives or alcohol as substitute solutions, and this in itself reminds them how far they are from the concept of "I can do all things through faith." Suspecting that the minister will only remind them of their inadequacy and demand that they depend upon a faith that they do not have serves as a rationalization for many people to keep their problems to themselves.

After a patient had said he had never gone to a minister with his problem, a student chaplain asked him why. The patient replied, "I guess I thought a minister would tell me that I had to stop using drugs." The student asked, "You don't think the minister should tell you to stop using drugs?"

"Well, it wouldn't be so bad if the preacher could give me something to take their place. I guess I thought there was nothing that could do for me what drugs do . . . so there was really no use for me to go sniveling to a preacher and just have him say that the whole thing was on me and that I was the one who had to make up my mind to quit."

No doubt many addicts would be willing to give up drugs if they had something of equal potency to substitute for drugs. The message of most religions, however, is that man should face life and not try to run and hide. The addict who feels overwhelmed, inadequate, and angry thinks he is completely at the mercy of circumstances that are hostile to him. He wants to run away. "Stand and fight" is just too much of a challenge for most addicts. The addict may be tired of the trouble he gets into through the use of illegal drugs, and he may say, "I want to quit." This does not mean that he is mature and able to face his difficulties. It usually means, "I'm tired of being chased and reprimanded by the authorities for my actions. I want someone either to make drug use legal or to give me some kind of substitute for opium."

One day I walked into the room of a patient, introduced myself, sat down. Before I could say anything, the patient let go with the following verbal blast: "How can you be so cruel? Here I am sixty-five years old, my wife is dead now for ten years. I'm physically sick. My children are married off, have kids of their own, don't want to have anything to do with me, and I don't want to have anything to do with them. They tend to their business and I tend to mine. I have to have medicine. I don't break any laws to get it. I have an old doctor who writes prescriptions for me. I take my medicine at home. I don't get out of the house except to go to the drugstore, and once a year get down to vote. You see I am a good man. I do what's expected, and I don't bother anybody. And you want me to stop using. You want to have me become aware of my pain and all the misery in the world, all the injustice. How can you be so cruel . . . and you call yourself a Christian?"

Visiting the minister may precipitate arrest.   Some addicts have said, "Addiction is not a spiritual problem, it is a medical problem. If I went to the preacher all he could do is say, 'You should stop,' but he couldn't take me off drugs. He'd have to call a doctor and doctors can mean trouble." When asked what he meant by "trouble," he went on to explain that any physician the minister might call would know all about addiction. The doctor would probably suggest that the addict go to the hospital. This might eventually reveal his addiction to the police, who would be curious about his source of drugs, and this would lead to his being charged with illegal activities. On the other hand, if the addict were to refuse the physician's suggestion to enter the hospital and run from the encounter, the minister and the doctor might decide that in his best interest they should call the police, who would arrest him for his own protection. Of course, the addict does not view such an arrest as being in his best interest. He interprets it to mean further rejection and punishment.

The code of the streets.   As has been mentioned in preceding chapters, most addicts come from the depressed, low economic, uneducated, overpopulated areas of large cities. Life in these areas seems to be built around survival and getting what few pleasures the individual can find. The young frustrated persons in such environments form groups—perhaps because there is strength in numbers, or because every individual needs to feel that he belongs to something. In order to belong to the group, the individual must adhere to the rules for living set down by the group. If the group is delinquent, then everyone in the group must become delinquent. If the group boasts of strength, then no one in the group dares to show any sign of weakness. Any weakness on the part of an individual reflects the weakness of the other members of the group. Therefore, no one in the group can admit to weakness or doubt or spiritual problems. Probably a person in this sort of a group never entertains the thought of going to a minister. If he did have the thought and brought it out into the open he would meet with so much hostility from the other group members that he could lose his status in the group. Even in a hospital setting, members of groups like this don't care to talk about religion. Sometimes in private discussions with a minister a patient may open up and express some of his feelings.

One addict said during a private conference, "I never had anything against ministers. If they are sincere in what they are trying to do I guess they are all right. No doubt they may help a lot of people. I just never thought that they could do anything for me and that I didn't need the kind of help that they can give. I always lived the 'swinging way' and didn't want to mess with that religious righteous stuff. So I just let them alone and expected them to let me alone."

Some persons may have been slightly exposed to religion as a young child, but received no encouragement at home to consider religion seriously as an important factor in living. As a result, these persons grow to adulthood with very little use for religion and consequently see no need to tell their problems to a minister.

"I seldom thought I had a problem. The purpose in using narcotics in the first place is to find peace and calm, and release from all problems. When I did have thoughts that maybe there was something wrong with me I would consider the possibility of getting into therapy . . . of course, this would be just a passing thought, and I would never do anything about it. I guess I never ever considered the possibility that I had a spiritual problem. In fact, I had always rebelled against religion anyway. I don't know how the rebellion got started. I just thought religion was a big lie told to the masses to keep them in line and I wasn't about to swallow anybody's lie. So-called 'religious people' that I knew were caught up in materialism, seeking to satisfy their own interests. I just didn't want any part of them. I suppose I was influenced by my father. He was religious, at least he said he was, but he didn't ever go to church. Mother went once in a while. I sometimes went to Sunday School. I had relatives who were very religious, to the point of fanaticism. They were anti-twentieth century. The children in this family seemed unhappy. They were not allowed any privileges, even to play with the other kids. They did though. They would slip off and do what they wanted to. They had to do undercover what other kids could do out in the open and without fear of punishment or judgment. I felt these kids were being cheated and all in the name of organized religion. Their religion was something that I viewed from a distance. I didn't like what I saw so I never thought in terms of any sort of personal involvement, so I suppose I never really entertained the idea of seeking help from a minister."

Understanding the Problem

Many pastors have experienced the dilapidated moocher or the professional panhandler who comes through town, stops by the church to see the pastor, solicits his prayers, relates a tale of woe, and pleads for a loan to tide him over until his situation gets better. Few ministers have had an addict come to them for a handout. Addicts usually stay away from ministers.

The addicts with whom I have talked, and who went to see a minister, said they were exhausted from running and hiding and using drugs, and wanted help. Knowing no place else to turn they sought out the minister, partly because they may have heard that ministers help people and second, because ministers are supposed to keep problems confidential.

Whatever the reason, some addicts do visit the minister. What are the things a minister should keep in mind when he is visited by an addict?

Physically sick. Usually the older addict is physically sick. He may have some chronic physical condition that may be painful. In addiction, his body has built up a tolerance to the drugs, and unless drugs are administered at regular intervals (in some instances as often as every three to four hours), the body begins to experience the uncomfortable abstinence syndrome. The addict knows that a shot of narcotics is always an immediate solution. It is an instant cure. But it has its problems. Drugs are illegal. The addict is in trouble every time he needs a fix. The question the addict may ask the minister is, "Do you know of an instant solution to my problems? A solution that will not get me into trouble?" The physical discomfort experienced by the addict when he is without drugs may be one of the motivating factors that drives him to seek help. His inability to tolerate this discomfort for a sustained period may also cause him to run from the minister if he suspects that the minister's suggested solution may involve time, patience, and self-control.

Emotionally sick. Although the body is physically addicted, the crucial effect of narcotic drugs is upon the emotions. The minister must keep in mind that his "well wishes" and "good advice" may be sufficient support for many people in his congregation. The addict, however, is often incapable of accepting advice, because he is usually so emotionally helpless that he cannot act upon a suggestion. Prior to his seeking help he may have put on an air of being competent to handle any situation. He can do all things through drugs that strengthen him. Of course, in reality he can't do everything. Drugs simply deaden his feelings to the point that he doesn't care whether he is adequate or not, and he just assumes that he is conqueror of all he surveys.

The addict may not even be able to sit still in the minister's office for more than a few minutes. If the minister wants a detailed history of the person and the development of his problem, he may not get one. To an invitation, "Sit down and tell me about yourself," the addict may reply, "Look man, I don't have time for that, are you going to help me or not?" This may mean that unless the minister has a ready solution (and who has?), the addict will be off and running.

The minister may know that he can only be of help to the person if the person can make himself available to be helped. Most addicts want help, but they find help difficult to accept on any terms other than their own.

Moving a little further in the area of the addict's emotional state as he confronts the minister, we see that essentially the addict is plagued with fear. One of the fears may be that of discovering that he is inadequate.

Persons prone to become addicted tend to be passive. Males may find it difficult to assume the masculine role. When told to act like a man, the male addict becomes highly indignant, for he wants so desperately to be a man. Usually, he has never had a close relationship with a man and simply does not know on an emotional level how a man should act and feel. This sort of person may possess all the outward manifestations of being a man, yet be paralyzed emotionally and function on a feeling level as a frustrated child. Before this sort of a person can be helped, he must see himself for what he is and begin to relate to other men, especially authoritative figures, on the basis of mutual understanding and respect. This area will be considered later in more detail. It is simply mentioned at this point to clarify one of the many problem areas of the addict who comes to see the minister. He is afraid to face feelings of inadequacy in terms of his identification—perhaps in his work and relationships with other people, and always in the area of assuming the responsible role of husband and father, if he is one.

I hope I have made clear the case that the addict is essentially a very weak person. He doesn't like to feel weak. He looks for something to make him feel better. Drugs do. They really do not make him feel better, they just deaden his capacity to feel anything— which is what he wants. When the addict says, "When I started using drugs I felt better than I ever felt in my life," he really means that while using drugs he feels less pain. Denied drugs, his ability to feel reality returns. Of course, he likes a pain-free existence. He therefore interprets denial of drugs to be a denial of his right to be comfortable. To him drugs are not a crutch, they are the "staff of life."

The addict comes to the minister seeking help, but he may also be expecting rejection. As was mentioned in an earlier chapter, the life histories of many addicted patients reveal not just one rejection, but many, especially during the developmental years. Seldom do we see an addict who has been consistently loved and accepted by important people in his life. If he had been loved and accepted he probably would not have become addicted. Persons with a history of rejection often have life patterns and ways of acting that continue to bring them rejection, and thus a vicious cycle is set up. Instead of being able to solicit understanding and support, they usually provoke those who would help—and end up with more rejections to their credit. Paradoxically, while looking for help, the addict continually seeks rejection. That's all he knows. If he finds a person who does not reject him, he will usually find a way to get rejected or to distort the relationship in his own mind until he can make himself believe that he is being rejected. The minister needs to be aware that just about anything he says or does will be interpreted by most addicted persons as rejection.

Being apprehended by the law is another fear that plagues the addict. This is a very peculiar fear, since the addict is in trouble with the law so much of the time. His fear is of being locked up, of experiencing abstinence syndrome "cold turkey" (without benefit of medical assistance), and of being denied drugs. After the discomfort of abstinence syndrome subsides, however, many addicts are able to adjust very readily to the rigidly supervised environment without the assistance of drugs. This area will be covered in more detail in two later chapters.

A loner. Usually the product of frustrated parents, he probably has never known a healthy relationship in his life. Unable to have a closeness with his parents, he probably has never been able to get close to anyone. The addict, if married, has probably been married several times. At the slightest conflict he has to run, since he is emotionally unable to stand the pain of conflict long enough to reach a solution. The older addict with a long history of addiction may be a father but has very little relationship with the children. Since he has been emotionally a child himself, he has always been in competition with his children and thus is unable to give them the support they need. In later years therefore, they usually do not want to have anything to do with their addict father. Most older addicts have no one who wants to put up with their whining, childish demands and they frequently end up living in a low rent, pay-by-day hotel . . . alone.

Alone in the world, the addict is also separated from God. Not in the sense that God has left him nor that the addict himself has made an actual break with God. God is simply a term the addict generally neither knows nor understands. The only power, the only reality the addict knows and can depend upon is drugs. Drugs never let the addict down. They always provide the feeling that they are supposed to. The addict sometimes finds that people do let him down. He hasn't seen God, nor does he think God has done anything significant in his life. If there really is a God, then why has He permitted the addict to have so many uncomfortable experiences? Then too, if there is a God, as everybody says there is, He is probably like the law. He would only judge and punish and deprive. So the addict is usually content to leave all the God stuff to somebody else.

Ambivalent about quitting. One would naturally assume that a person going to a minister about a problem has seriously contemplated doing something about his problem. Most addicts whom I have known said that many times they thought of quitting drugs. When asked why they had wanted to stop, they gave reasons that were mostly social in nature. Drugs were costing them too much money. They couldn't always get drugs when they needed them. They didn't like the constant threat of being apprehended by the law for illegal possession or some other crime connected with narcotics. Their families were putting too much pressure on them. Seldom have I heard an addict say, "I wanted to quit because I became concerned with what life is all about. I wondered if real meaning came as a result of blotting out all anxiety and feelings of inadequacy, or if really to be alive meant to face up to life and all its problems, try to understand myself, and try to make a better go of living and getting along with people."

Always in character. The minister should keep in mind that the addict who comes to him is limited in the roles he can play and probably won't change character for the benefit of the minister. One reason the addict has few friends and relationships is that he has used and manipulated people until they no longer want to have anything to do with him. It's sometimes difficult for the minister to believe that the nice-looking, smooth-talking, polite man who sits before him may have sold all the family appliances or stolen and hocked anything of value to purchase narcotic drugs for his own use. If he can get the money by being a smooth-talking, nice man he will never resort to degrading methods, but people finally get wise to smooth talkers. When people tell him they are through with him he has to run to the next source . . . and the next . . . and the next. If he finds no one he can manipulate to get money, he becomes forced to take what he can get, where he can get it. When the addict comes to the minister it does not necessarily mean that he has finally seen the error of his ways and intends to lead a new life under the direction of the minister. In most instances the addict thinks the minister will be easy to convince and that he can use him. One addict related the following story.

"I guess I should be ashamed taking advantage of a minister like I did, but I was desperate and, after all, he's just a man like all the other people I've had to cheat over the years in my quest for drugs. I was getting sick, needed a shot, and was stone broke. My connection wasn't about to extend me credit. He just didn't deal that way. Having approached him so many times before, needing a fix and having no money, I knew I would only get a kick in the face if I went to him without any money. He was a terrible guy, but that's off the story. I went to this preacher. Like I say, I was desperate, so I leveled with him. Well, I told him I was an addict. I said that I was trying desperately to get off drugs. I had been praying and all that, but I was really having it rough. I told him that I had been to a doctor and the doctor had told me to taper off, that should I try to quit abruptly I might die. I said that the doctor had given me a prescription, at no charge, but would not give me the drugs as he said he wasn't in the charity business. I told the minister that I just didn't have the money to get the prescription filled. Then I put it to the preacher. I told him I needed advice and counsel as well as prayers and wondered if he would be my resource person? I said I would like to see him regularly to discuss my problems, learn to pray, and draw upon religious resources—and even asked him if he thought I might someday be accepted by the people in his church. This got to him. He said, 'Why of course we will accept you.' I was so grateful, he thought. I may have even shed a tear or so. Then I asked him if he thought he could help me with the withdrawal by making me a loan of a few dollars. He went for his pocket, and as he did I could taste the drug. He asked how much it would take? I was tempted to run it up, but I said that just seven, no more than ten dollars would be necessary to purchase sufficient quantity to effect withdrawal. He handed me the money. I wanted to run, but I knew if I did that would be the end of it. He would know I was faking. He might follow after me or even worse, he might call the police. So I led off by asking him what time I could see him the next day. This seemed to please him. He set the time. I thanked him and asked him to remember me in his prayers . . . and split (left). That was the last I saw of him. You know, I never told him my name. I suppose if he had asked me I would probably have made one up."

The addicted person who confronts the pastor is physically sick, perhaps with some actual physical malady, but always threatened with the sickness of abstinence syndrome if his drug intake is reduced.

The addict is emotionally sick. The condition is usually of long duration, dating back to early environmental experiences. He is filled with a multitude of fears and finds a retreat in narcotics.

He is usually all alone. He has ruined most of his opportunities for relationships, and when he gets to the minister he may be at his last source of hope.

The pastor should expect the addict to relate to him in much the same way in which he relates to everybody else. He shouldn't be too shocked or annoyed if the addict tries to manipulate him. Furthermore, he shouldn't berate himself if the addict is able to manipulate him and get to him, because manipulation and cunning is the full-time vocation of many addicts. Besides, you don't become an expert until you can show a history of being taken. The man who hasn't fallen prey, has not been close enough to the problem to do any good.

What To Do

Listen, don't lecture.   The addicted person who sits before the minister is as bound physically and emotionally as a person can be. In the language of the addict he is "hooked." A person who is hooked does not have to be told the evils of narcotics. He knows all the problems involved in using drugs—in a more personal and intimate way than the minister could ever know. If the minister were to ask, "Don't you know what narcotic drugs will do to you?" the addict would probably feel like saying, "Preacher, what I know, you wouldn't believe." It is at this point the addict begins to feel that the interview is going sour, and if the minister even suggests that with a little will power and determination addiction can be overcome, then the addict is convinced that the minister just doesn't know what he is talking about.

The minister should try as best he can to listen to what the addict has to say. He should listen for important facts. If the person is not a member of his congregation, then who is he? Where does he live? What family does he have? How long has be been using drugs? What did he take drugs for? What specific drug or drugs is he taking? How long since he had the last dose? If the person does not give the information readily, then the minister should ask him. The minister needs to get as many facts as he can at this point to help him determine what he must do. Of course, the minister will not want to ask needless questions. The main considerations are: Who is this person? Where from? Belongs to whom? What has he been taking? How long? If the person has been addicted to an opium derivative or one of the synthetic preparations for a long time he may need drugs every three to six hours. If he misses a dose, he will begin to show withdrawal symptoms within a few hours. The minister needs to know this, because if the person begins to show symptoms he may have a very sick person on his hands.

Don't flount knowledge of slang jargon. The addict will not be impressed if the minister uses terms like "weed," "H," "bennies," "yellowjackets," "red birds." In most instances, the minister's knowledge of these terms is only hearsay. It has been my experience that persons will speak in a language that I can understand. If they happen to use a slang term, they usually quickly translate so that I know what they mean. The goal is to encourage the addict to become a "square" and use our language, not for the minister to become "hip" and use the language of the addict.

Use of Scripture and prayer. A few pastors have reported instances of addicts being "cured" (the pastor's term) of drugs through counseling, and the use of Scripture and prayers. In no instance (of such cases) that I have heard was the pastor exactly sure what drugs the person was taking or the duration of the addiction. I will not make an evaluation because enough facts are not known.

The typical approach used by these pastors in dealing with the addicts is as follows:

The first step is to get the person to admit that he is powerless under some power or force that controls him; second, he has to affirm that God is sufficient to break the power that binds him; and third, that God wants to help him and will, if the person will let God have control of his life. The fourth step is to read selected Scripture passages. The one most frequently mentioned is the Ninety-first Psalm. One pastor reported that an addict, after several readings of the Psalm and having professed that God could and would break his addiction, began to weep, then sobbed heavily, and finally shouted that God had given the victory and he was cured. The pastor stated the man became a member of his church and had no problem with drugs thereafter. The addict in question was not available to validate the story or to give the pertinent facts mentioned earlier.

A few pastors have reported success through praying for addicts. Again, these pastors had very little information on the history of the addict's problem. Generally, when the addict came to them or they heard of him and went to see him, they used the same method, that is, confronting the person about his sinful condition, affirming God's power to change the person, and reading Scripture and praying for the deliverance of the person.

"As you know I was here a few months ago, but I only stayed a short while. At that time I was using six to eight ounces of paregoric a day. When I got to the hospital, I had a terrible time withdrawing. [The records verify his statement.] But I just didn't stay long enough to really get cured. [He checked out in about two months.] I wasn't out very long until I was using again. My mother and several friends who are very religious began to pray for me and told me that they were asking other people to pray for me, too. One friend sent a minister to see me. He talked to me awhile, read the Bible to me, and prayed. He came back a few days later and repeated the same thing. All this time I was using paregoric. The minister came by one Sunday evening and took me to church. At the end of the service they asked that people who wanted to be prayed for should come to the front and kneel. I went. I prayed that God deliver me from drugs. Several others prayed with me. I told God that He could deliver me if He would and that I knew He could. I began to get a full, happy feeling. It was like a similar feeling I had one time when I was a teenager attending a church summer camp, during the consecration service. I went home after church that Sunday evening feeling very good. When it came time for me to fix the paregoric I did. I guess God really hadn't cured me and since it was time for me to take the fix I had better fix or else I would start having symptoms. I took the usual amount and nothing happened. I didn't get a high feeling, no sick feeling, nothing. I thought it a little peculiar that nothing had happened. Later I fixed again, this time I used a little more. I guess it must have been about eight ounces and again nothing happened. I began to get concerned. Later I used ten ounces. I fixed twice and nothing happened. I also took amphetamine and seconal tablets, but they didn't take either. I could not get a good feeling, I couldn't get sick, just nothing. By this time I was completely bewildered and beginning to get scared. Something really must have happened to me, but I didn't know what. Using as much narcotic as I was, I was really scared. I called the hospital and told the doctor what had happened and he told me to come on out and he would admit me. I did. I was taking more drugs than when I was previously admitted, but this time I had no withdrawal." [Records show that he showed no symptoms and was given no medication.]

After about three weeks the patient was discharged and returned to the church where he had found the experience. He became an active worker.

This story is something of a puzzle. I would be the last person to doubt the power of God, but I do not think one isolated instance of an unusual phenomenon should motivate us to discard reason and propriety. To disregard medical knowledge in favor of purely religious procedure in the treatment of narcotic addiction is to place God in an unfair position. For instance, seizures are not uncommon during withdrawal from a heavy barbiturate habit. Unless experienced assistance is given, a series of such seizures could be fatal. The minister who does not face his responsibility of getting medical help for such cases is guilty of gross error. The minister should be concerned with the well-being of people, and the minister does not play magic games when a person's life is at stake.

This is precisely why the minister needs to get facts from the addict as to the length of his addiction, and to what drugs—so that he will know the urgency of medical care.

Utilizing the family. Though the addict, through his own manipulation and irresponsibility may have isolated himself from his family, he is still a person in the community. Sometimes the addict may not want to reveal to a minister or anyone else his family ties and responsibilities. Usually the addict feels guilt because of the way he has misused his family—mother, father, wife, or children. He does not want them brought into the situation for fear they will bring out all his misbehavior, and he will have to face himself in front of the family and the minister-counselor. In other instances, the person may have kept his addiction hidden from the family. He may be concerned with the embarrassment to the family of having an addict in the unit, but the addict's concern is usually in terms of the embarrassment to himself. It is often no surprise to the family that the person in question is in trouble. In fact, relatives sometimes say, "I thought something was the matter."

Unless the minister helps the addict to realign himself with his family, he contributes to the perpetuation of the schism and the addict is not essentially helped. I would suggest, then, if at all possible, that the family should be involved in the treatment process, whatever it turns out to be. Any relationship established between a person and the addict to the exclusion of important members of the addict's family constellation only aids in drawing stronger lines of separation. As the minister gets better acquainted with the many aspects involved in motivation for drug addiction, he will discover that feelings of separation are very close to the source. The minister should think of himself in terms of a bridge builder. This sometimes involves a lot of his time. It may demand more time than he can spare. It may require more understanding of distressing family situations than he possesses. He should not hesitate to enlist the services of professionally trained persons in the community to assist in the total rehabilitation of the addict and the family. I am suggesting other service agencies that may employ clinically trained social workers; for example, family service, community welfare organizations, various psychiatric clinics sponsored by the community or the county. If the minister assumes that the person became addicted, that he developed his problem in a vacuum, and that his rehabilitation is only of a personal nature, then the minister is in for a very disappointing experience.

Medical treatment.   If the minister is to be of real assistance to the addict, he may have to become very directive and insist that he get medical treatment. I agree with Armen Jorjorian, "No meaningful therapeutic counseling can be done while the addict is controlled by drugs—first he must be withdrawn from his physical dependence upon narcotic drugs."[1]

Getting the addict to accept treatment is no simple task. In the first place, the addict usually is not capable of making the decision; otherwise, he would already have made it. Looking at case histories of

[1] Armen Jorjorian, "Drug Addiction and the Pastor," *Pastoral Psychology*, February, 1952.

addicts, one finds that, as a rule, addicts have difficulty making good decisions. Many of their more important decisions could be interpreted psychologically as "acting out their unconscious feelings," especially feelings of inadequacy and hostility, instead of reaching conclusions on the basis of good conscious reason and logic. Though the addict may be of normal intelligence, his emotional development is usually so thwarted that he is unable to deal successfully with stressful situations. Deciding to accept treatment is a stressful situation.

As the minister begins to understand the addict's inability to tolerate stress, he can more accurately perceive the addict's anxiety about being withdrawn. The addict feels not only the physical pain, but also a legion of emotional conflicts. Unable to tolerate them, he will want to run for relief. Treatment of addiction does not promise immediate relief. His ambivalence about quitting drugs, mentioned earlier, becomes more pronounced as a counselor presses for the addict to decide for treatment. If left to his own decision, the addict will probably run for another fix.

For the addict's own well-being the minister may have to assume some responsibility and call in a medical resource to assist in the decision to hospitalize the person. The physician is able to make a diagnosis and to admit the addict to a hospital. If the minister does not have a physician in his congregation to whom he can go with special problems such as drug addiction, he should make it his business to seek out a physician in the community and establish such a relationship, so that he has someone to call on in case of emergencies.

Hopefully, the minister, the doctor, the family will decide that hospitalization is the best immediate solution. Withdrawal from narcotic drugs can be accomplished in a local hospital. However, most hospitals can only effect a physical withdrawal. There may be a special hospital in the area for addicts and alcoholics. If so, these special hospitals are usually equipped and staffed to do more than just withdraw the patients.

The most effective treatment for narcotic drug addiction is available at one of the two Federal narcotic hospitals, located at Fort Worth, Texas and Lexington, Kentucky. I would suggest that the minister encourage the addict to seek admission to one of these hospitals and see that he gets there if admission is granted. I would further suggest that the family set up some sort of controls to keep the person in the hospital until some important changes can take place in his life. Admission procedures to the Federal hospitals will be discussed in a later chapter.

Finally, and this is as a last resort (no other alternatives being available) the addict can be withdrawn in jail. Sometimes families who feel unable to control the addict, and believe that eventually he will hurt himself, call authorities to take the addict into custody. For the minister, I would suggest this method only if no other solution seems possible.

CHAPTER SEVEN

HOSPITALIZATION As THERAPY

Most addicts need treatment in a hospital, although some have been reported to have been withdrawn from drugs without hospitalization. The minister will be concerned with where and how to get the addict hospitalized.

Local General Hospitalization

Some addicts have been treated for addiction in local general hospitals. After withdrawal was accomplished in the hospital, some were able to resume their responsibilities. In general hospitals, the addict may be withdrawn in several ways. Physicians generally prescribe a substitute narcotic drug for the drug used by the addict. The substitute drug is administered in diminishing amounts until the addict is not receiving any drug at all. This can be usually accomplished within a week. To be admitted to a hospital, the addict will have to be under the care of a physician who alone has the authority to prescribe drugs.

Physical withdrawal from the drugs is about the extent of treatment received in a general hospital. Unfortunately, physicians and general hospitals are often reluctant to accept addicts for treatment.

Dr. James Lowry states, "The treatment of a hospitalized narcotic addict is a relatively simple and a relatively complex procedure. Treatment of the physical addiction resulting from the pharmacological properties of the opiates is relatively simple. The treatment of the psychological addiction and of the basic mental disorder is relatively complex."[1]

The physical withdrawal usually accomplished in a general hos-

[1] James V. Lowry, "Hospital Treatment of the Narcotic Addict," *Federal Probation*, December, 1956.

pital deals with only a part of the addict's problem. The treatment of the emotional, social, and vocational difficulties requires resources that may not be available in a general hospital.

Treatment in the Federal Hospitals

In the United States there are two Federal hospitals for the treatment of narcotic addiction. The U.S. Public Health Service Hospital, Lexington, Kentucky, was opened in June, 1935. The other hospital, located at Fort Worth, Texas, was opened in 1938.

Established for the purpose of treating Federal prisoners and probationers, and addicts committed from the District of Columbia, these two hospitals were also authorized to accept voluntary patients addicted to narcotic drugs as defined by Federal law. The law included all narcotic drugs whose sale is regulated by Federal narcotic laws. Persons addicted only to barbiturates or alcohol are not eligible for admission. If, in addition to barbiturates or alcohol, the person is also addicted to a drug included in the federal narcotic laws, he is then eligible for treatment.

Prisoners and probationers are sent to the hospital by the Federal courts. Volunteer patients are admitted through making application. Applications for admission may be obtained by writing to the Medical Officer in Charge of the Hospital. The completed application, when returned to the hospital, is processed, and admission is granted on the basis of available bed space. The minister should neither send nor take a person to one of the hospitals without authorization for admission. Preferably, the minister should seek assistance of a physician to refer a patient to one of the Public Health Service Hospitals.

The Lexington hospital accepts volunteer females from any state and volunteer males from east of the Mississippi River.

The Fort Worth hospital does not accept female addicts. It accepts volunteer males from west of the Mississippi River.

The informed minister should have a working knowledge of the treatment program of these two hospitals for two reasons: (1) Since he may be encouraging addicts to apply for admission, his understanding of what will happen to the person during treatment will assist him to dispel many of the fears of addicts contemplating hospitalization. (2) Some addicts who come to the minister for help may have been previously hospitalized for addiction at one of these two hospitals but signed themselves out of the hospital against medical advice. It is not uncommon for an addict who has run away from treatment to distort the reality of what happened, especially if the listener is uninformed and might believe his story.

The purpose of this chapter is to orient the pastor to the treatment program of these two hospitals. Though the programs are similar, this chapter will essenitally describe the Fort Worth program.

The application.   Treatment of the volunteer addict begins when he writes or calls the hospital for an application for admission. The patient is not necessarily in treatment if someone else writes or calls for him. Many patients who were leaving against medical advice (many within a day or so after admission) have told me that it had not been their idea to come to the hospital in the first place. When asked what they meant, they said, "I neither wrote for the application nor filled it out. It was their idea, not mine. I think I'm all right, and I don't need to be in this hospital." In many instances, these persons did leave the hospital but were back before very long—not as volunteers. They were back under Federal sentence, or perhaps again as volunteers, but under pressure of a state charge if they left the hospital against medical advice. If the patient writes for the application himself and takes care of completing and returning it, the chances are greater that he will stay long enough to benefit from the treatment program. The application must be filled in properly. It is not sufficient for the applicant just to state that he is an addict and sign his name. He must answer all questions. If the patient can handle this much responsibility, it is a good indication that he is seriously considering hospitalization.

Admission.   When the addict enters the hospital gate he is received by a member of the security staff who thoroughly understands the physical and emotional stress of the addict awaiting treatment. This staff member's friendliness and reassurance not only influence the addict but also dispel many of the fears of relatives or friends who may have brought the addict to the hospital for treatment.

The first official step is to verify the authorization for admission. This is accomplished by checking identification, the letter the addict has previously received authorizing admission, and verification from the medical records that the patient is authorized and is arriving on the assigned date. It is at this point, if all papers are in order, that the addict becomes a patient.

Relatives or friends who accompany patients to the hospital and arrive during the normal working day of 8:00 A.M. to 4:30 P.M. are encouraged to meet with a member of the social service staff. This meeting has a twofold purpose: first, to assist the family or friends to understand the treatment program and what will be happening to the patient during his stay in the hospital, and, second, to learn as much about the patient as possible in order that the hospital may better understand him—his needs as well as his responsibilities.

The patient is asked if he has any drugs in his possession. This is not a senseless question. A drug-free environment is essential for the treatment of addiction. Hence, every effort is made to keep the hospital free of contraband drugs. This is both threatening as well as reassuring to the addict. On the one hand, he knows that "No drugs" means he will be withdrawn and will have to face many of his fears and anxieties. At the same time, he knows very well that to be free of drugs he must be in an environment where none can be obtained by his schemes and manipulations. Many addicts take a last fix just prior to coming through the gate of the hospital. One patient took a large dose of barbiturates just before coming to the hospital. He had to be helped out of the taxicab when he arrived at the gate. While the security aide was calling to verify the patient's admission, the patient fainted. The aide called the physician, who came to the gate. Seeing the patient's comatose condition, he had him rushed to the infirmary unit on a stretcher. In the infirmary, the aides removed his clothes while the doctor began emergency treatment. Within a few days the crisis was over and he was transferred to the withdrawal ward.

Some try to hide drugs along the fence of the hospital grounds, to be picked up later. Some try to conceal drugs in the hollowed heels of shoes, in fountain pens, wooden legs, or in any manner they can think of that might be overlooked by security. It is for the patient's well-being that he is asked to place all his belongings in a sack and is given a "pat down" (superficial search to make sure the patient has surrendered all articles that might contain contraband). The sack is sealed in his presence and is handed to another security aide, who escorts the patient to the admission unit.

The admission unit is a series of rooms. In the first room the patient's admission papers are processed. He is given a receipt for his valuables in the sack. All narcotics or paraphernalia are removed to be analyzed and subsequently destroyed. His valuables are locked in a safe. Some articles will be given to him later upon his request. Everything except contraband is returned to the patient when he is discharged. His money is deposited with the agent cashier of the hospital. Patients cannot carry money in the hospital. They are issued scrip which they can spend in the patients' commissary to purchase cigarettes, refreshments, and personal toiletries.

In the second room the patient is asked to remove his clothing and is carefully checked to make sure he has not taped drugs or money to his body. He must then shower and shave, after which he is issued pajamas and a robe and moved to the next room.

In the examining room he meets the physician, who takes a medical history, including history of his addiction, and proceeds to give him a complete physical examination, including rectal examination. Addicts attempt to smuggle drugs in strange ways.

The patient is then photographed for identification purposes and is escorted to an intensive treatment ward where he begins the process of withdrawing from drugs.

Withdrawal. On the withdrawal ward the patient is introduced to the staff, assigned a bed, and issued hospital clothing that he may wear in place of the pajamas and robe issued to him in the admission unit. He is given typhoid and tetanus immunizations and is assured that when he shows sufficient withdrawal symptoms he will be given medication. He is told that he must make his own bed and assist with keeping the ward clean, especially in the area of his bed.

Usually on the second day the patient is taken to the laboratory for several tests, that is, of blood and urine. He also gets a chest X ray and is taken to the dental clinic for a dental examination.

When the patient begins to show symptoms of second-grade withdrawal (gooseflesh, dilated pupils) he is given syrup of methodone (liquid preparation of a narcotic drug) in sufficient quantity to make him feel comfortable and relieve his symptoms and signs of withdrawal. This dosage is maintained for three days. By the end of three days the patient's habit has been changed to a methodone habit. Methodone treatment is used because it is easier to administer (liquid), and methodone withdrawal is easier for the patient. After three days of the same level of methodone, the dosage is reduced by five milligrams per day until he is receiving nothing. At this point the physical addiction is over. The patient will not have any further withdrawal symptoms. However, it may take several weeks for his body to recondition itself.

Withdrawal from barbiturates is different from opiate withdrawal. Patients taking barbiturates in amounts of five hundred milligrams or four nembutal tablets per day are given two-tenths of a gram of pentobarbital every six hours for twenty-four hours. If the patient has not become intoxicated in that time period, his dosage is raised one-tenth of a gram per dose per day until he does become intoxicated. Intoxication is a drunken state in which the patient has difficulty keeping his equilibrium and shows slurred speech. Intoxication indicates the patient's tolerance to the drug he has been taking. The dosage is then reduced by one-tenth of a gram per day until he is getting no more medication. Withdrawal from barbiturates is done carefully and slowly because dangerous abstinence symptoms of delirium or convulsions may occur without warning.

Withdrawal from heroin and the opiate derivatives takes from four days to a week. Withdrawal from barbiturates may take two weeks or more, depending upon the size of the habit as well as the physical condition of the patient. Patients in extremely poor physical condition may be withdrawn at a slower rate at the discretion of the physician. Patients in barbiturate withdrawal are assigned a mattress on the floor instead of a bed. This is to prevent the patient from falling off a bed while he is intoxicated.

During the week or more on the withdrawal unit, patients go to the main dining room for their meals. They are taken on a tour of several areas of the hospital to learn the location of the occupational therapy shops, recreation areas, libraries, chapel, and the patients' commissary.

On the ward there are meetings, led by the physician, the social worker, the nurse, and the aides, to discuss problems of addiction, living on the ward, what comes next in treatment, and personal problems and complaints.

Members of the recreation staff visit the ward to assist patients in occupying their time while on this ward. In addition to the special games brought by the recreation staff, facilities are on the ward—

dominoes, checkers, cards, television, and so forth. Patients are encouraged to write to friends and relatives. A few do. Some patients spend their time talking with staff members. Most stay to themselves, except when they have to go to a staff member to obtain medication.

Not everyone admitted to this ward finishes withdrawal. Of all the volunteers admitted to the hospital, approximately one-third leave against medical advice within the first two weeks of treatment or before they are completely withdrawn from drugs. Another third leave (against medical advice) within the first month of treatment. About one-third stay from five to ten months, the minimum of time required for a patient to be discharged as "improved."

Upon completion of withdrawal, patients are transferred to one of three continued-treatment wards. Though all patients eat, attend school, and work together, living areas of prisoner patients and probationers are separate from the volunteers. This is because volunteer patients irritate prisoners. The prisoners may have to stay in the hospital one year or several, depending on their sentences. The volunteers can sign themselves out at any time they so desire. In terms of the prisoner patients, "The 'vol' has the key in his pocket."

Before the actual transfer to a continued-treatment ward, the physician of the ward meets with the new patients to outline the rules and regulations of his ward. A nurse explains the procedures to obtain clean clothing and to dispose of dirty laundry. Patients are informed of the various ward duties that they are expected to perform. They are told how to report for sick call and how to obtain medication as prescribed by the physician. They are instructed where to pick up mail and how to register complaints.

Orientation. The patient's first week on the continued-treatment ward is given over to a complete orientation . . . he to the hospital and the hospital to him. After being assigned a bed, the patient reports to the testing center to be given a series of tests. He will be given Intelligence Quotient, School Achievement, Vocational Interest, and Employment Aptitude tests. Results of these tests will be evaluated and used in the planning of the treatment program.

Next, the patient meets the chief of the Addiction Service to hear explained many of the resources available during his hospital stay. The patient is asked to check his areas of interest and list the activities for which he would like to be considered. If he is interested in individual and/or group therapy, a vocational training program, school, church attendance, Alcoholics Anonymous, or self-help groups, he so indicates on the card. The patient is often reluctant to commit himself by stating what he wants to try to accomplish during his stay in the hospital. Many patients say, "Well, I just want to look over the place for awhile, and then I will make up my mind as to just what I want to do." During this meeting the chief tries to deal with the resistance of the patient and encourages him to commit himself, whether he is to take part in the program or whether he is waiting for the first opportunity to sign himself out of the hospital. These cards are then given to the person responsible for that activity, who interviews the patient and enrolls him in it.

When the patients meet with the chief of the Addiction Service, they have the opportunity to ask questions thus far not answered to their satisfaction. The chief explains in greater detail the over-all program of the hospital.

Patients then meet with heads or representatives of the various services, who give the patient information that he will need in order to function within the hospital. For example, a representative of the food service explains the procedure of eating in the dining hall. Of course, the patient has already been eating in the dining hall, but was taken over by an aide on the withdrawal ward and told exactly where to sit. Now the patient still goes to eat with his particular ward but is permitted to sit in an area of his choice. He is also told he may have special diets upon request of his physician. In general, he is told things that all must consider when several hundred men are eating together.

During this week, he meets with a member of the security staff. In a community of eight hundred there are certain rules that must be followed in order that the best interests of all will be served. One hospital goal is to help patients to live more effectively, and one way to live more effectively is to abide by the rules. The security officer explains that should the patient not accept his responsibility of living in community, certain privileges will be denied him, for example, loss of movie privileges for a time.

Included in the week of orientation is a meeting with the chaplain of his faith. The chaplain answers his questions, acquaints him with the religious activities of his faith in the hospital, and encourages his participation.

Before the week is over, the patient is called in by his physician for a psychiatric evaluation. The physician takes a history of the patient's family, his early developmental years, schooling, employment, social adjustment, and mental status. After evaluating the patient's mental status, his life history, and the extent of his drug problem, the physician recommends a particular course of treatment for the patient.

The big push. Having completed withdrawal, recuperated further physically from the drug, and oriented to the hospital, the patient is ready for the "big push." The total effort of the hospital is brought to focus upon the patient and his problems. Everything in the hospital is directed toward helping him mature so that he can function effectively and productively without having to rely upon narcotic drugs for support. The term given to this all-out effort is *milieu therapy*.

Although every patient is involved in milieu therapy, only about one-fourth of the total number of patients are in individual psychotherapy with their physician. Two factors are involved here. One is the shortage of physicians; the other is the lack of motivation of the patient for individual therapy. About 75 percent of the patients are in group counseling, with either a physician or a trained group leader. The groups meet once a week. In these groups, patients discuss everything—from early childhood experiences that may have influenced their behavior to problems of living in a hospital, to what they plan to do when they leave the hospital.

At the end of the week of orientation, each patient meets with the vocational counselor, who assigns the patient to his first job in the hospital. Every patient who is able must work. He is usually given a choice of several areas in which he can work. This choice depends upon jobs available at that time, as well as the needs of the hospital. For example, the food service requires the largest number of patient-workers. Operation of this area is essential. Many patients therefore, spend their first tour of duty in the kitchen. After ninety days each patient is entitled to request a job change should he desire it. Change will depend upon the availability of the job he wants as well as his reasons for wanting to make a change.

It is not uncommon for patients to have difficulty on their hospital job assignments. Many are not used to working at a regular job. They are not used to taking orders and carrying out their responsibilities. They show a history of many jobs of short duration, usually having left each before they had time to master it. Patients attribute their job instability to the work having been too hard or to their inability to get along with their bosses. It follows, then, that they would have difficulty in the hospital, since they must work. Work supervisors are trained in their various trade skills. They also understand the problems of the patients. The work supervisor, in addition to being a boss, tries to be a counselor and a friend. The supervisor is aware that the patient may constantly test the relationship by performing poorly or getting into trouble. In such instances, the supervisor confronts the patient and tries to deal with him as openly and fairly as possible. The supervisor is required to make monthly reports on the patient's progress in his job. The supervisor usually meets with the patient to discuss how he is doing. The reports are sent to the vocational placement supervisor, who in turn makes reports to the physician on the patient's progress.

The hospital does not assign the patient to a job just to keep him occupied during his hospitalization. The hospital is interested in the patient's total educational and vocational rehabilitation.

Schooling and vocational ability of patients varies from having no formal education or vocational skills to having received the Ph.D. and certification in several medical specialties. The hospital attempts to provide a constructive experience for every patient, regardless of the level of his academic or vocational achievement.

The tests given during the orientation program play an important role in planning the patient's program. Patients who test below the fifth-grade level are required to attend school. Their work assignment is planned so that they are free to attend school in the afternoons. After a period of instruction they are tested again and, if they meet fifth-grade requirements, may sign up on their own to continue study until the completion of the eighth-grade level. Patients who have not completed their high school education and have reached their twenty-first birthday, after due course of study are entitled to take a high school equivalency test. Certificates are issued by the State Department of Education on the basis of passing the General Educational Development tests.

Remedial courses are designed to assist patients who evidence specific academic weaknesses, such as inability to read, write, and calculate through the eighth grade level. Some academic courses are offered to assist patients prepare for particular trades; for example, applied mathematics in preparation for electrical work or engineering. Classroom instruction is also offered in accounting, typing, commercial art, drafting, radio and television servicing, and watch repair. In addition, patients enrolled in apprentice on-the-job training courses receive related theory instruction in the classroom in carpentry, plumbing, machine shop, electricity, sheet metal, and refrigeration and air conditioning.

For those with higher aspirations, the hospital encourages enrollment in a correspondence course of study in an accredited college or university.

The patient is pushed to make a maximum adjustment in education and work. He is encouraged to explore new job possibilities and to begin formal study toward preparing himself to work in his chosen field upon his release from the hospital.

Many patients keep in touch after their discharge from the hospital, to inform us of their progress in the trades they may have learned while in the hospital. One patient was admitted to the hospital after approximately ten years of difficulty with narcotics. Before coming to the hospital he had worked as a sales clerk and a mechanic. He did not do well in either. While in the hospital, he learned X-ray work as well as laboratory work. Upon his release the hospital assisted him in getting a position as an X-ray technician. After three years he is still doing well and is free of narcotics. Another patient, who learned the plumbing trade, was able to find work through a state employment service and, according to reports of his probation officer, is working satisfactorily after a year. Still another patient, who learned to design, cut materials, and sew in our garment industry, opened a small garment factory of his own after his discharge from the hospital.

In a recent study, 52 percent of a group of discharged patients were productively employed.

Addict patients also have problems with leisure time. To help patients learn to use their leisure time constructively, the hospital maintains a large, well-equipped occupational therapy service for instruction in general arts and crafts, woodworking, metal, and plastics. Classes are held each day and in the evenings for the benefit of those patients who have work assignments during the day. Attendance in occupational therapy classes is voluntary, except when the patient is assigned to occupational therapy on prescription by his psychiatrist.

In the general arts and crafts shop are tools and equipment for leathercraft, frame and loom weaving, basketry, metal tooling, aluminum etching, stenciling, copper enameling, mosaics, clay modeling and ceramics, rake knitting, beadwork, cord knotting, shellcraft, and drawing (finger, charcoal, pastel watercolor, oils).

In the woodworking, plastic, and metal shop are tools and equipment for cabinet making (tables, chairs, magazine racks, flower boxes, television and phonograph cabinets, bookcases, picture frames); turning bowls, plates, candlesticks, and lamps on lathes; wood carving (trays, drums); and plastics (mobiles, bowls, trays, lamps, planters, dominoes, paperweights, internal carvings for plaques).

Primarily, occupational therapy attempts to provide:

1. Opportunity to develop leisure-time hobby interests.
2. Opportunity to work together in a group—companionship.
3. Opportunity to create something for self, or a gift for the family.
4. Opportunity to explore pleasure received in making articles.

For patients with pronounced character disorders (some bordering on the psychotic) treatment is directed toward:

1. Providing opportunity for acceptable expression of aggression and relief of unconscious guilt feelings through socially acceptable creative accomplishments.
2. Improving insight into personal problems.
3. Adjusting to hospitalization.

In addition to the occupational therapies, a recreation service is concerned with teaching patients to use leisure time constructively during and after hospitalization and to learn to form and maintain social relationships. Entertainment is essential for patients who are confined. The tensions that all of us feel under normal conditions are magnified during confinement. Unless acceptable ways are found for these feelings to be expressed, they will be vented in other ways. Many of the scheduled activities—softball and basketball, for example—give the patients an opportunity to yell at the umpire. This is acceptable in our society, but is is not always acceptable to yell at authority. In many of the sports, patients have an opportunity to compete with others. The type of patient in the Public Health Service Hospital is not one to compete. Passive, such individuals tend to be watchers rather than participators. They are afraid of losing. They think people will laugh at them if they do not excel in an activity. To assist the patient, games of competition are organized. There are inter-ward softball, basketball, and volleyball teams; occasionally teams of staff members play the patients, often to the embarrassment of the staff. Teams from community and civic organizations, churches, schools, and other institutions come to the hospital to compete with hospital teams. On occasion, hospital teams are permitted to make a trip outside the hospital to play a community team on its home court or field.

Many patients spend considerable time exercising and working out in one of the two gymnasiums. Body building is one of the favorite activities of patients. A patient may work three times as hard building his body as he would on a work assignment, but to him the reward is greater. He cannot always see satisfaction in a job well done, but he can see the results of muscles that have grown and he knows that other people can see them, too. The bigger his muscles, the bigger he thinks people will think he is.

As important as any part of his hospital treatment is the patient's need to get along with other people. We find that it is easier for people to relate in a play setting than an authoritarian setting. For example, many of the student chaplains report that at times they have found it almost impossible to engage a patient in conversation on a ward or in his work area, or in the chaplain's office. If they called him into the office, the patient would be tense and unable to share any of himself, even if the student chaplains' intentions were only to be friendly. Students report that if they walk into one of the recreation areas, watch awhile, maybe pick up a pool cue and lean lightly on it, somebody will probably invite them to shoot a game. If the student will keep his mind on the game (he will probably have to concentrate very hard or be beaten by the patient), the patient may begin to open up a little and reveal something about himself. Some students say that their best relationships with patients started at a pool table.

The Recreation Service provides two 35-millimeter films per week.

These are recent films, and often patients are pleasantly surprised to find that a film they are to see is also scheduled for the same night at one of the movie houses in the community.

Special groups, such as civic or fraternal clubs, schools, and churches, come to the hospital to bring entertainment programs. The musicians' union is a frequent visitor. Several different garden clubs visit the hospital to bring gifts to patients and to assist with decorating the wards during festive seasons. The Grey Ladies of the Red Cross visit the hospital six days a week to talk and play games with, write letters for, and serve cake to patients. Numerous social activities—ward parties, special group parties, and coffee hours—give patients opportunity for socialization. Not infrequently there will be a formal coffee hour or tea. For such occasions, a table is properly set according to the demands of etiquette. Very nice china and silverware are used on these occasions. Patients are taught how to act at such a function. At one coffee hour a patient commented, "This is real nice. You know this is the first time in my life I have ever drank coffee out of a real china cup." He wasn't the only one in the group who had never had such an experience, nor will he be the last. Our purpose in the hospital is to teach as much as we can while we can.

The hospital staff knows that the big push to help the patient must be focused on the patient, but we may not be completely effective if we limit our concerns to the patient alone. A favorite phrase of the chief social worker at the hospital is, "People do not become sick in a vacuum." This is especially true with addicts. As was pointed out in earlier chapters, many factors contribute to a person's becoming addicted, not the least of which is poor relationships with important people in his life. Patients in the hospital often want to separate themselves from their families. Usually there has been a great deal of tension and stress between the addict and members of his family. His illegal activities with narcotic drugs were no doubt a source of great embarrassment to his family. One patient, twenty years old, and the son of a minister said, "It must have been tough on the old man to come down to the jail and get me out. I must have been arrested at least a dozen times on small beefs (charges), and he would come bail me out. I would promise to do better, but before I knew it, there I was again, locked up and calling for help. I guess he didn't like those police cars driving by the house all the time, either. A couple of times they stopped, officers came in the house with a search warrant think-ing I had a stash of drugs. This sure must have put him in a bind with the congregation, but he never did anything about it. He just begged me to try to do better. I was surprised one day when he walked in the house with the police and told them to arrest me. He told me that he had taken all he could take, that he hadn't been able to do anything with me, and that he was turning me over to some-body whom he hoped could make a man out of me. Well, that's how I ended up here."

When a social service worker interviews the patient in an effort to determine his family ties, the patient sometimes says, "Leave them out of this. I got myself into trouble and I don't want to bring my family into it." Others are reluctant for social workers to correspond with relatives, because the patient thinks that he will lose control of the situation. He is used to going to one person and manipulating for what he wants, and then to another. He is afraid that, should the hospital authorities and his family meet, they might work together toward putting an end to his scheming and manipulating.

Unfortunately, relatives do not always cooperate. Many times rela-tives will not answer letters. They feel that the hospital is trying to pry into their privacy. Others are too embarrassed, or too mad at the patient to want to cooperate. Others are so afraid of being manipu-lated by the patients that they just want to stay away from them as much as they can. Still others are so guilt ridden about the patient's condition that they are most susceptible to the patient's manipula-tions; frequently these persons cannot put up any resistance to a patient's signing himself out against medical advice.

In an attempt to bring the family and patient together on a more stable basis, the social service worker works closely with the patient, encouraging him to correspond with the family, and evaluates the relationship with him. A social service worker also visits with the family when they come to visit the patient. Important issues are often discussed at conferences between the social service worker, the pa-tient and the family. The social worker is there to facilitate discussion of certain important questions that both patient and family might tend to smooth over. The more family conflicts that are resolved, the greater are the patient's chances of staying free of narcotic drugs upon discharge.

As mentioned earlier, most of our patients come from an economically poor situation. To illustrate, one patient was making about thirty dollars per week prior to his admission to the hospital, most of which he spent on narcotic drugs. He was married and had six children ranging in ages from a few months to seven years. His wife had little formal education and was unskilled. He had no relatives, and her relatives were all receiving support from a welfare agency. When the patient began to get the narcotic out of his system and became aware of his family's needs, he became anxious and upset and, instead of participating in the hospital program, he defied and evaded interaction with staff. The social service staff was able to contact in the patient's community a welfare agency that, in turn, was able to obtain help for the family. With the family receiving some aid, the patient was able to settle down, adjust to the hospital, and begin to work on his problems.

The pastor may be wondering if we make any attempt to deal with the patient in terms of his spiritual needs. The answer is "Yes," but a qualified "Yes." Only a small percentage of the patients who come to the hospital have had any significant religious experience or training. Those who were baptized and attended Sunday School usually stopped going by the time they were seven or eight, if they continued that long. It is easy then to understand the patient's lack of religious awareness. In the second place, the patient's activities since he stopped attending church were usually socially unacceptable; therefore, he separated himself from the "righteous" people. Patients new to the hospital often try to steer clear of the chaplain unless, of course, they have a job they want him to do. For example, they may want him to write a letter to convince someone that the patient is a nice guy, or to obtain some kind of information from somebody. A chaplain will write on occasion, but usually he confronts the patient with his reluctance to write and encourages him to do his own correspondence. If the patient pleads "You can do it so much better," the chaplain will reply, "There's no better time than now for you to learn."

In general, the attitude toward religion that we see in the hospital is, "If I ever think it has anything to offer me, I might give it a try." The patient interprets everything in terms of what it has to offer him. This is contrary to most religious thinking. Most religions think in terms of a person becoming aware of who he is, his relationship to God, and his responsibilities to his fellow men. Outside the hospital, the addict never stood still long enough to be confronted. Inside the hospital, he tries to avoid it as long as he can. The whole hospital program, however, is directed toward making him become aware of himself and of his relationship to others. As the chaplains see patients making progress in any area of hospital treatment, they give thanks.

As a patient becomes more aware of himself and more socially conscious, his interest in religion increases. Usually he will show interest in studying some abstract philosophy that keeps him separated from the mainstream of organized religion until he can get a better look at the Church and Church people and decide whether or not he will be accepted. For those who do become interested in religious activities, there are, within the hospital, worship services of three major faith groups, Bible studies, discussion groups, prayer groups, and choir groups. Individual religious counseling is available. Every effort is made to encourage patients to participate, but attendance at any religious activity is voluntary.

The hospital maintains a library of more than eight thousand volumes. The patient has his choice of fiction, the classics, autobiographies, et al. The library subscribes to many popular and cultural magazines, and newspapers from the hometowns of most patients. For patients confined to the infirmary, the library provides bedside service. A cart filled with the most popular books and magazines is brought to this unit several times weekly to supply reading material to patients. A Great Books Club is sponsored by the library in an attempt to enlarge the patient's literary understanding.

For many years Addicts Anonymous has played an important role in the hospital treatment program. With the assistance of Alcoholics Anonymous groups from the community, the hospital club has discovered that the teaching and principles of Alcoholics Anonymous fit the needs of the addict. Patients accept the responsibility of directing the activities of the club, with a minimum of supervision from staff. The community groups not only come to the hospital to share their experiences and encourage patients—they accept the patient when he is discharged from the hospital and offer relationship while he makes the important step of adjusting himself to society.

Discharge. Discharge of a patient is as crucial as admission.

The entire hospital program is aimed at getting the patient ready for this event. Though many volunteer patients leave the hospital against medical advice, some stay for an "improved" discharge. Discharge is considered at a patient-staff conference that initially helps the patient set goals and eventually assists him to evaluate his achievements.

Within two weeks after a patient is transferred to a continued-treatment ward, he has his first "staffing." This conference, chaired by the Chief of the Addiction Service, is attended by the patient's social worker, a psychologist, the vocational placement officer, nurses and aides from the ward, a security worker, a work supervisor, a chaplain, and the patient's physician. The physician reviews the patient's history and psychiatric evaluation. Members of the staff share their findings about the patient, and a program including short- and long-term goals is set. The patient participates in this conference. The staff believes that very little change will take place in the patient unless he is part of the planning. As the patient discusses with the staff what he intends to do during his hospitalization, the staff may make firm suggestions that he consider more things than he planned. This initial conference ends with the staff encouraging the patient to get to work on the goals that have been set.

In about two months he is staffed again—this time to see how much progress he is making. The physician reviews the patient's problem and the goals that were originally set—and gives his opinion of the patient's progress. The ward nurse and aide report on the patient's ability to get along with the other patients, his willingness to carry out ward responsibilities, and his participation in ward meetings. If the patient is in group counseling, the leader will indicate the patient's participation. Does the patient talk? Does he show himself to other members of the group? Does he get involved in their concerns? His work supervisor evaluates him in terms of work habits and characteristics. How much supervision does he need? Does he get the job done and how much time does it require? Does he try? Is he accurate? Does he get to work on time? How does he get along with others on the job? His social worker reports on correspondence with the family and confronts the patient in terms of his participation in repairing the probably damaged relationships at home. At this second staffing the patient is usually encouraged to continue in the program and is told that he will be reviewed again in a few months.

Some patients become so anxious that they check out of the hospital before they are ready. Repeatedly, we hear patients say, "I've been off drugs now for a couple of months. I can handle my problems, so there is no further need for me to stay. I know drugs will always be a threat, so I'll just stay away from them. I'm cured, and all I need to do now is leave the hospital and start living." Most patients who leave at this point are quite unrealistic about their emotional stability as well as their actual plans for starting life again. A case in point: A patient decided to sign out against medical advice. He had stayed in the hospital about two months. He visited the chaplain as he was leaving and asked for money, as he put it, "To tide him over until he found something." The patient, in his early sixties with a 40-year history of addiction, was unable to work because of a back ailment of long duration. He had no relatives and no place to go. The chaplain urged him to remain in the hospital until arrangements could be made to find him a place to stay. Obtaining work for him seemed quite unreasonable. The patient signed out anyway. Reports subsequently received indicated that he started using paregoric the day he was discharged.

The hospital does not underestimate the problem of drug usage, but attempts to focus more upon the patient himself. The patient would rather look at external factors than himself. The hospital continues to emphasize to the patient that he is the problem and push him toward making changes.

By the third staffing, hopefully, the patient is making progress. Specifically the staff looks for:

1. Assurance that the patient is beginning to feel comfortable with himself. That he is becoming self-reliant and learning to appreciate himself.
2. Evidence that he is learning to get along with other people, making friends with individuals, and becoming able to be a member of a group.
3. The ability to handle everyday life situations with a minimum of anxiety. Not blowing his top or having to use drugs.
4. The ability to control impulses and think in terms of long-range goals.

As the patient is able to maintain a level of successful experiences the planning for discharge becomes more active. Involving the patient in discharge planning is crucial "It [the need for such patient involvement] is rediscovered, in retrospect, every time one of our carefully worked-out discharge or parole plans is rejected by an 'ungrateful patient' or a plan fails to work successfully despite our attention to every legal requirement. The essential lack consists in our ignoring the patient himself. It is our failure to enlist his participation. He has no interest in someone else's plan."[2] We therefore try to get the patient to commit himself, to write to relatives to solicit their support, and to find a place to live. We have him write to parole or probation officers and to previous or prospective employers to inquire about work.

When the patient has made the internal changes mentioned earlier and deals realistically with the physical essentials, when he attempts to repair relationships, finds a place to live, and obtains a job, we consider him ready for discharge.

[2] Arthur K. Berliner, "The Helping Process in a Hospital for Narcotic Addicts," *Federal Probation*, 1962.

CHAPTER EIGHT

OTHER GROUPS HELPING The ADDICT

The two Federal hospitals treat only a proportion of the addicts in the United States. Many are sent to state or Federal correctional institutions. Some of those incarcerated are given educational, vocational, and other rehabilitation services. If the released offender is on parole, he is supervised for a time after his release from the institution.

Some addicts are cared for by nongovernmental agencies and groups. The programs of these groups vary according to their own orientation and understanding of the problem of addiction. This chapter briefly describes some of these groups and their programs.

Narcotics Anonymous

Narcotics Anonymous was organized in 1948. It was patterned after Alcoholics Anonymous. By substituting the term *narcotics* for *alcohol*, Narcotics Anonymous has been able to utilize the Alcoholics Anonymous theory of rehabilitation.

Members meet in groups to discuss their problems with drugs and to apply the principles of Alcoholics Anonymous (Narcotics Anonymous) to their lives. However, Narcotics Anonymous has not met with the same degree of success as has Alcoholics Anonymous. Outside the correctional institutions only a few Narcotics Anonymous Clubs have been functioning for a considerable period of time. Many reasons are given for their lack of success. Some reasons are:

1. Addicts themselves say that discussing drugs in all-addict groups is in itself a hazard for the addict. Many relate incidents of meeting in just such groups—and after talking about drugs for some time the whole group went out and fixed.

2. Sometimes pushers go to addict meetings. They may start out by saying that they want to quit using drugs themselves, but after the discussion gets started, they begin to talk about how good it would be to have a fix. Other addicts report of pushers waiting outside the door of a meeting to taunt and tease the groups as they leave the meeting and tell them that they will be waiting for them when they need a fix.

3. Sometimes members of the narcotic squad attend Narcotics Anonymous meetings. This inhibits addicts from talking about themselves. One of the objectives of the Alcoholics Anonymous Program is to get the alcoholic up before the group as soon as he is able to stand and encourage him to tell all about his problem with alcohol. If the addict gets up and tells all about his problem with drugs, and is heard by a policeman, he may run the risk of being arrested. The reader will want to remember that the alcoholic can tell all about going down to the corner package store and purchasing liquor, sharing it with anyone, and drinking it himself until he went into a stupor. So long as he had money to pay for the liquor and did not steal it or create a disturbance while drinking it, nothing is said as far as the law is concerned. The addict, however, cannot tell of his going out to buy drugs. If he does, he is confessing to a crime (possession of illegal drugs is both a state and Federal offense). He also implicates the seller (state and Federal offense for selling illegal drugs).

4. Some addicts say that, as a general rule, addicts are so dependent that they are unable to provide the strength essential to maintaining a group. The addict seems to run from stress and tension and is unable to tolerate conflict that arises in groups. After a confrontation in a group meeting the addict will miss a meeting or two, then begin to rationalize (at which he is very adept). Before he knows it, he is using drugs again and feels too ashamed to return to the group.

Considering the length of time Narcotics Anonymous has been in existence and the fact that there are so few active Narcotics Anonymous groups, it is obvious that Narcotics Anonymous has not met with the great success in rehabilitating the narcotic addict that the parent group, Alcoholics Anonymous, has enjoyed in rehabilitating the alcoholic. In my opinion, this lack of success is not a reflection upon the principles or the philosophy of Narcotics Anonymous. Rather, it is due to the differences in the personalities of the addict and alcoholic.

Narcotics Anonymous can probably be of significant value if there are a few reasonably strong persons in the group who can set struc-tures and limitations for the others. These leaders must be free from drugs. They must be strongly motivated to remain free of drugs. They must be able to confront others in the group and challenge them to a life without narcotic drugs. If an addict will give himself over to the program of Narcotics Anonymous and accept and practice the "Twelve Steps," the program will work and the addict will find a way of life free of narcotic drugs.

One of the most significant facets of the Narcotics Anonymous program is its companion group, Nar-anon. This group is made up of the wife or husband, parents or children of addicts. The purpose of their meeting is to learn about the problems of addiction and how they can more effectively live with and be helpful to the addict.

I have had several conversations with Nar-anons. All have been very enthusiastic about their program as well as that of Narcotics Anonymous. The parents of a young addict once said, "It's the great-est thing that ever happened to us. We are actually learning about ourselves in Nar-anon. Now that we are beginning to understand ourselves, we are beginning to understand our son. We have noticed that his relationship with us is changing. He is sharing more with us. We are aware that it is just not him that is changing. We are changing too, and we like it."

Alcoholics Anonymous

Because there are so few Narcotics Anonymous groups outside institutions, some addicts have attended Alcoholics Anonymous meetings. It has been my experience that most Alcoholics Anonymous groups welcome the opportunity to help the addict. They consider the addict to be just another powerless, enslaved person. They believe that the only difference between the alcoholic and the addict is in the masters they serve. And, they want to give the addict every oppor-tunity to accept the philosophy of Alcoholics Anonymous, and to begin to practice it with them.

There is so much in print about Alcoholics Anonymous that I shall not elaborate on its history or its principles. For the pastor who wants to learn more about Alcoholics Anonymous, I would recommend the book *Alcoholics Anonymous.*[1] The pastor wanting to understand the alcoholic and his problems better will find *Helping the Alcoholic and His Family*[2] a most helpful resource.

Many alcoholics have some understanding of the problems of the narcotic addict. In nearly every Alcoholics Anonymous meeting I have attended there have been persons who reported use of barbiturates or amphetamine tablets in addition to their use of alcohol. They may have used the tablets to overcome an alcoholic hangover. Others used tablets when alcohol was not available. Some stated they quit drinking alcohol and began using tablets only. Many said they were at first very pleased with themselves to be able to stop using alcohol. They became concerned again, however, when they discovered that they had only traded one master for another. Persons with such experiences have some understanding of the addict and his problem and can be of great assistance to him.

I would recommend that the pastor not refer an addict to an Alcoholics Anonymous group until the addict has been withdrawn from drugs in a hospital. In the first place, the addict usually needs an enforced drug-free environment in order to stop using. As long as drugs are available, it is most difficult for him to stop. Second, when the addict is fixed (in limited amounts) he looks and acts normal. Unlike the alcoholic, it is difficult to determine that the addict is using drugs. While he is under the influence of a drug, he is not helped by Alcoholics Anonymous or anybody else.

The following story was told to me: An addict had attended a small Alcoholics Anonymous club for more than two months. The group met several times a week in a very informal setting. The addict was an active participant in the group. He discussed his problems with drugs. He claimed to know his personality defects and boasted of having conquered the narcotic habit. He became so confident that the group began to suspect something was amiss. They challenged his claim of abstinence. He denied using anything. They continued to pressure him. Finally, he admitted using narcotics daily. He was told that the group couldn't be of any help to him unless he stopped using. He stopped attending the group.

[1] *Alcoholics Anonymous* (New York: Alcoholics Anonymous Inc., 1949).
[2] Thomas Shipp, *Helping the Alcoholic and His Family* (Englewood Cliffs, N.J.: Prentice-Hall, Inc., 1963).

Addicts discharged from a hospital or institution will find the door open at Alcoholics Anonymous. I have heard many addicts make excuses for not attending Alcoholics Anonymous. Some claimed they were not welcomed and that alcoholics look down on addicts. In both instances I would think the opposite to be true. Most addicts don't want to face their problems, and they find excuses to keep away from a place where they might have to do so. In Alcoholics Anonymous the addict will have to deal with himself. He may have to admit to himself and others that the image he has maintained is false. He may have to admit his dependency and need for support from something outside himself. He will be expected to become involved in assisting others with their problems.

Many addicts who have been free of narcotic drugs for five to seven years have told me that they owe their narcotic-free life to Alcoholics Anonymous.

Teen Challenge

Teen Challenge is the result of the driving conviction of David Wilkerson who says, "It is impossible to cure a drug addict without God."[3] I am inclined to think that most of the people in the helping professions believe they are something like assistants in the Divine Process of healing, although they might not so state publicly. But David Wilkerson makes no apology that his efforts are underwritten by God. Nor is he eager to accept an addict into his program unless the person realizes he has a personal need for God to make a change in his life. Mr. Wilkerson states, "Those who are not willing to accept Him [God] cannot be kept. Those who refuse God's power and the simple Bible way of salvation soon land in jail. When they are desperate enough they will call on God."[4]

Teen Challenge got its start in 1958 when Mr. Wilkerson went to New York City in an attempt to help seven boys who had been indicted for murder. He had been reading LIFE magazine, which carried the Michael Farmer story. David said, "I was dumbfounded by a thought that sprang suddenly into my head—full-

[3] David Wilkerson, "Positive Cure for Drug Addiction" (New York: Teen Challenge, 1963), p. 18.
[4] David Wilkerson, "Teen Challenge Marches On," The Pentecostal Evangel, No. 2590, Dec. 29, 1963, p. 10.

blown—as though it had come into me from somewhere else. Go to New York City and help those boys."[5]

David went to New York City but was of little assistance to the seven. What he eventually accomplished was perhaps even greater than success in manipulating the course of events for the seven would have been. He was able to gain rapport with many of the teen-age gangs that roamed the streets. He preached to them on street corners, in vacant lots, ball parks, any place he could get them together. He became acutely aware of the needs of the rootless teen-agers, who form groups for identity, false security, and status and get into mischief beyond their years. This young preacher, raised by a Fundamentalist family, was quickly oriented to life on the streets of Brooklyn. He saw the drinking, fighting, promiscuity, and drug addiction. He saw teen-agers in their quest for pleasure, as well as their search for some meaning in a seemingly hopeless situation, turn to narcotic drugs for solace. He also learned that while these youngsters were addicted to drugs they were not readily available to the message of new life and hope he preached. He made a special effort, therefore, to reach this group.

Although Mr. Wilkerson's attempts to help the seven boys was unsuccessful the publicity he received because of his efforts was a factor in helping him to reach other youngsters. A few of the gangs approached him and wanted to know about his interest in the seven boys. Some accepted his reasons, but others rejected them, thinking he was working an angle. When he began to talk about religion, many who first listened turned away because they were not interested. He began to realize that if he was to make any headway, he must reach the gang leaders. This was to be no simple task. The gang leaders, as a rule, resisted his challenge. Gang leaders had to be tough. They considered any show of religious interest to be a sign of weakness. Most of them ignored Mr. Wilkerson.

He kept working, and eventually some youngsters responded. Some were helped and returned to the streets to tell the others what had happened to them. Some of these reformed addicts were able to convince other addicts with whom Mr. Wilkerson had been unsuccessful, and through their success, his program got under way.

By means of gifts from individuals and churches, Mr. Wilkerson

[5] David Wilkerson, *The Cross and the Switch Blade* (New York: Bernard Geis Associates, 1963), p. 4.

was able to purchase a house on Clinton Avenue in Brooklyn. This house became the headquarters from which he launched his program to help the addict.

The addicts who responded to Mr. Wilkerson's preaching, plus other addicts attracted by "street services," were brought to the house on Clinton Avenue. Many were addicted at the time, and they soon began to have symptoms of withdrawal. Some were not able to stay and had to leave. Mr. Wilkerson and his staff did whatever they could for the withdrawing addict. Treatment usually consisted of reading Scripture to him, singing hymns, praying for him, and encouraging the addict to pray for himself. They tried to stay with the addict at all times. During the early days of the program, when it was impossible for someone to be with every addict experiencing withdrawal, they would put a tape recorder beside his bed, to play Scripture and hymns.

As the addict began to overcome the withdrawal symptoms, the workers began to stress his need to confess his sin to God, so that God could forgive him and start him upon a new life. Many did not understand what the workers were talking about, but some responded and obeyed the instructions, and their attitude began to change.

As youngsters began to change as a result of the efforts of Mr. Wilkerson and his workers, the community began to take notice. Law enforcement agencies and probation officers began to make referrals.

As the number of referrals increased, Mr. Wilkerson became aware of the need for a more extensive program. He began to look for a place, outside of New York City, to which he could send addicts for further rehabilitation. Again with gifts from interested persons and churches, Mr. Wilkerson opened the second unit of Teen Challenge on a farm at Rehersburg, Pennsylvania. Aware that many teen-agers had never been off the city streets in their life, Mr. Wilkerson believed the farm would be a rich experience for them. In a recent interview, teen-age addicts living on the farms commented: "Sure beats the Harlem streets," "This is the best place for us; we are serving the Lord here," "I know the Lord is watching over me here, but I wasn't sure when I was in the city. It's rough here, but I made it."[6]

[6] *The New York Times,* February 16, 1964.

Addicts now are admitted to Teen Challenge upon referral of hospitals, clinics, physicians, ministers, and law enforcement or probation officers. Before an addict can be admitted, he must present a health certificate indicating his physical fitness. No person with venereal disease is admitted.

Once admitted, the addict is withdrawn without medication, because Teen Challenge believes experiencing the sickness of withdrawal will be a deterrent to future use of drugs. The addict is asked to promise that he will stay with Teen Challenge six months. No smoking is allowed. Teen Challenge believes if a person cannot overcome a small habit such as using tobacco, he cannot overcome a strong drug like heroin.

Addicts generally stay about two weeks at the center and then are taken to the farm at Rehersburg. There, a staff of ministers and reformed addicts conduct classes in Bible, language, agriculture, woodwork, music, and other subjects. After six to eight months, some are sent to Bible schools or colleges for further study. Others are returned to the city to obtain jobs. Some continue in the organization and assume staff positions.

Those who return to the city to work are assisted by job-placement agencies. All are referred to local churches to continue in their spiritual growth.

The results of Teen Challenge seem encouraging. Mr. Wilkerson reports that hundreds of addicts have been rehabilitated. Criteria for rehabilitation were not revealed to me. Mr. Wilkerson reports that many of his staff members are converted addicts. Several have been working closely with him for over two years. According to Mr. Wilkerson, Teen Challenge keeps a close check on all persons who have been through the program.

Several features of the Teen Challenge program have special significance for helping the addict:

1. Every applicant is interviewed by a committee of ministers and rehabilitated addicts to determine his desire to stop using drugs. In a conversation with me, Mr. Wilkerson said that only one out of ten is accepted. Those accepted must state a belief that God can and will cure their addiction. The applicant must be willing to stay six months and to give up smoking.

2. The entire staff is of one mind in its approach to the addict as well as its goals for him. Its members have all had similar religious

experiences, and their aim is that the addict have such an experience. They believe that as the addict has the religious experience his life will so change that he will no longer need drugs. Mr. Wilkerson calls the experience, "The Baptism of the Holy Spirit." He explains the phenomenon in his book and gives many examples of its effectiveness.[7]

3. When the addict is discharged from Teen Challenge he is placed in a church situation where he finds acceptance and encouragement. His past record of addiction is not a factor in his relationship with the congregation. Because of the spiritual experience, the church group believes the individual is a new creature. His old habits no longer bind him, and the congregation accepts him on the basis of his changes.

During 1963 the program has greatly expanded. Centers have been opened in five cities in this country; another is in Toronto, Canada.

Synanon

The thrust behind the Synanon Movement is its founder, Charles Dederich, who says of himself, "I wanted to be a big man. I wanted to make history, I always wanted to build a better mousetrap."[8]

Though not in the mousetrap business, Mr. Dederich has worked intensely in helping drug addicts. The Synanon Program, only six years old, boasts of more than three hundred clean addicts, living in Synanon Centers in four cities. I do not know the proportion of addict dropout after entering the program.

According to Mr. Dederich, the intention of the program is to "Bring about moral regeneration through the process of education. It is not that we teach anything, but the people in the program learn something. All we try to do is provide a situation in which people can learn to live."[9]

Synanon began to develop in 1958, when several addicts started visiting Mr. Dederich for companionship. An ex-alcoholic, he was

[7] Wilkerson, *The Cross and the Switch Blade.*
[8] Daniel Casriel, *So Fair a House: The Story of Synanon* (Englewood Cliffs, N.J.: Prentice-Hall, Inc., 1963), p. 25.
[9] Robert Zimmerman, "Synanon, State Seek Same Goals," *The San Diego Union,* January 9, 1964, p. 24.

very active in Alcoholics Anonymous as a speaker and also a "Twelve Step Worker" (one who makes a personal visit on alcoholics who are attempting to stop drinking). Having experienced several financial setbacks, Mr. Dederich had used the last of his funds to rent an apartment. As the number of visitors to his apartment grew, the discussions became louder and the record-playing sessions noisier. Finally, the landlord requested Mr. Dederich to move.

The evicted group pooled their financial resources and rented a store-front building in the amusement park area of Santa Monica, California. This building served as a clubhouse for alcoholics and addicts who wanted fellowship. It also became a dwelling, as people moved in with their few possessions. This usually amounted to the clothing they had on at the time. Since they had no money nor any other place to go, they reasoned they might as well stay with "Chuck" until something better came along.

The major problem of this group was staying alive—with very little money and no means of support it had a difficult time. Yet in spite of the hardship, a community began to develop.

Perhaps the most significant activity was the group sessions held several times a week. In these sessions, everyone was encouraged to express his true feelings. Anything short of violence was permitted. These sessions developed through a process of experimentation. First, "nondirective" meetings were tried, in which participants talked about anything they wanted to. There was no formally designated leadership in the group. This method was found to be unsatisfactory, and the responsibility for leadership was assigned to various group members. The leader would make a formal presentation on some worthwhile subject, then the others would enter the discussion. Finally, Mr. Dederich discovered the most satisfactory meetings were those in which he assumed rigid control over the group. Dederich is a genial, domineering person; when he speaks, the others take notice. He not only raises questions with the members in the group, but he gives directions that he expects them to follow. He said of this procedure, "By the end of July, 1958, I knew I had something that would work with addicts. I knew it."[10]

Dederich discovered that the addict needs a firm but understand-

[10] Casriel, *op. cit.*, p. 25.

ing authority figure to set limits for him and hold him within those limits. Said Dederich, "Psychologically, I knew the addict was emotionally immature, a child. I assumed they were like children and treated them as such."[11]

According to Dederich, the first few months were touch and go. He was responsible for the physical well-being of all who lived at the club. In addition to the financial problem, a break developed between the alcoholics and the addicts. Dederich sided with the addicts. He said of the situation, "The alcoholics were self-centered and not thinking of the group as a whole. They'd put ten cents on the mantel, then consume gallons of coffee. Also, they were too preoccupied with salvation, spiritualism and God. I was trying to run Synanon as a social scientist and psychiatrist would. I didn't like the religious overtones. I felt that Synanon didn't need serenity; we had too much work to do. So I told the alcoholics to get lost."[12] Most of the alcoholics did leave. A few remained in the revised program. Some are still living in Synanon at the present time. The major emphasis shifted to the addict.

Initially, very little control was exerted over the addicts who came to Synanon. They could go when and where they pleased. On occasion, four or five would leave together and, before they returned to Synanon, they would get fixed. During those early days, according to Dederich, no one in the group remained drug-free for more than two or three weeks at a time. He learned that, as a rule, addicts do not possess sufficient strength or motivation to abstain from occasional use. He had to make sure Synanon was drug-free. Addicts were no longer permitted to leave the house until they had been in the program for several months, and then only with Dederich's permission and in the company of some senior member of the group. Anyone who was suspected of a violation was quizzed at a meeting when all Synanon members were present. The humiliation of such an experience helped to prevent the situation from recurring.

Dederich developed the following working premises about addicts:

1. Addicted people should not be blamed for their predicament.
2. They can be praised or punished, but not with hostility.

[11] Ibid., p. 24.
[12] Ibid., p. 27.

3. The addict is like a child and is unable to handle a job or money.
4. They have to be inspired in love and loyalty because they have neither.
5. They have no conscience, no morality—no sense of moral responsibility, and therefore no blame. They should not be attacked.

The number of addicts who came to Synanon increased.

In August, 1959, Synanon moved into an old National Guard armory on the beach in Santa Monica. Most of the rent for the first month was paid by an actor's guild that had an interest in the Synanon Movement. The community of Santa Monica did not readily accept the addict rehabilitation center and made several unsuccessful attempts either to close Synanon or to have it moved elsewhere.

In addition to the Santa Monica unit, Synanon operates centers in New Haven, Connecticut; San Diego, California, and the Nevada State Prison. The last was started after the warden heard of the program in Santa Monica and thought it might work in the prison setting. After consulting with Charles Dederich, the warden turned an entire cellblock over to the Synanon group.

After visiting the Santa Monica unit of Synanon and discussing the program with Charles Dederich, it seems to me that its effectiveness is the result of six features:

1. *The intake.* Everyone who applies for admission is screened very carefully. Screening is done by several of the older members. The purpose of the screening is to determine motivation of the applicant. Synanon does not want everyone who wants to come in. Synanon has learned from experience that only those who have a strong determination to rehabilitate themselves will do so. Others will leave at the first conflict. Synanon believes it is better for the program to weed out these persons at the beginning. Another factor bearing upon the intake is the financial stress each person places upon the program. They cannot afford to waste money on people who are not going to stay.

Synanon does not take an addict if he is there because someone told him to go. I have heard of several instances in which people sent addicts to Synanon—only to be refused. Dederich said to me, "We don't want to make it look like we are inviting the person in. We don't care whether he gets in or not. If he wants to get in, he's practically got to break the door down." Each person admitted is usually charged. Some who have no money are admitted without charge. Others who have reserves of money are expected to pay according to what the committee feels would determine the applicant's motivation. A Scripture reference that Dederich might accept as being applicable to this situation is Matt. 6:21, "For where your treasure is, there will your heart be also."

2. *Withdrawal at Synanon.* Addicts are withdrawn without benefit of any medication. Synanon believes the addict's decision to stop using and to face the experience of withdrawal is an important step in his rehabilitation. They feel if he cannot face the sickness and frustration encountered during withdrawal, he will probably not be able to stand more intense frustrations later on. Second, according to Dederich, many of the addicts who come to Synanon are not addicted at the time. He says of many who are addicted upon arrival that their addiction is more psychological than physical.

During the time of my visit to Synanon, several persons were reportedly being withdrawn in the living-room unit of the armory. It was like a party. Twenty or thirty people were moving about the room. Some were singing; others were reading poetry aloud. Several little groups were talking and laughing. Nearly everyone was drinking coffee and smoking cigarettes. Sometimes persons become sick and have to be put to bed, but generally they are kept out in the living room, where life is going on. Synanon believes that friendly conversation, the music, plus the activity of the group, help to keep down the anxiety the addict experiences as his body adjusts to functioning without drugs.

3. *Work program.* As soon as the addict is physically able he is given an assignment. The addict's first job is usually one of the less desirable chores, such as scrubbing the floors or cleaning the rest rooms. Since there is no paid staff, members have to do all the work, with the most humbling jobs being given to the newcomers. The lowly assignments supposedly have therapeutic value. Dederich said, "We put them in their place and tell them if they ever want to get anywhere it will be up to them. . . ." New members are watched very closely to see that they do their assignment right. They are not

permitted to "goof off." If they do not take their jobs seriously they will be reprimanded and will not be promoted to better jobs.

In time, provided he has handled his job responsibly, the initiate may be assigned other duties. As mentioned earlier, everything is done by the members themselves, from cleaning to cooking to caring for the clothing. Quoting Dederich again, "It's a hell of a job to keep this community going. We have to do everything ourselves. If anybody lets down, somebody else has to do the added work—we just can't have that."[13]

4. *The sessions.* The group sessions are perhaps one of the cornerstones of the program. Originally called seminars, the name was changed when a member who was unable to say the word seminar used the word "synanon." The word made a hit with the group, hence the name of the program. In these sessions, members air their views about themselves, others in Synanon, or other important people in their lives. Complete honesty is encouraged. Members thus not only gain insight into themselves; they really see others in the group. In addition to the regularly scheduled sessions, any member can request a session if he has something he wants to talk out, or if he wants to confront someone in the group.

5. *Esprit de corps.* I was deeply impressed with the attitude of the people who were living in the Synanon House. They felt as though they belonged to a very select society and were very proud to belong. A few expressed joy at being clean of narcotic drugs, but most were elated over belonging to a new experiment, a new community within our society. Essentially, Synanon is a way of life. It is a community unto itself. The members live together, they work for each other, they are completely dependent upon one another, and in that particular setting, they are free of narcotic drugs. There seems to be little concern among members as to how they will do when they get into the larger community. Most of them are dealing with the day-to-day problems they experience in the Synanon environment. Many will be living in the house for several years. Those living in Synanon are assured of a drug-free, productive life as long as Synanon survives and they continue in the program.

6. *The man.* In my opinion, there would be no Synanon without

13 *Ibid.*

Charles Dederich. No doubt many strong personalities have assisted Synanon to become of age. The units in other cities are directed by persons from the original group and, according to reports, their work is excellent. However, I do not think Synanon would have made it through the lean years had it not been for Charles Dederich.

The Narcotics Committee
of
East Harlem Protestant Parish

East Harlem Protestant Parish represents a broad concept of the Church ministering to a community. The parish area is the heavily populated East Harlem section of New York City. Privately financed, but with an advisory board made up of representatives of seven Protestant denominations and certain other Protestant groups, East Harlem Protestant Parish provides several parish services in addition to facilities for corporate worship.

One of the services is the Narcotics Committee. This special committee was organized in 1956, although staff and members of East Harlem Protestant Parish had been ministering to addicted persons since 1950. The unit is located in a building having a store front. There is space enough in the unit for several offices and a recreation-meeting room. It is open during certain hours of the day to give psychiatric, medical, and legal services and to provide recreational and social activities to persons addicted to narcotic drugs.

The committee includes several professional persons: a lawyer, a psychiatrist, a sociologist, a hospital referral worker, and others. Although the committee is sponsored by the parish, not everyone on the committee holds the same religious views. The purpose of the committee is to make a positive contribution to persons who use drugs, regardless of their religious views or practices.

The work of the committee is within a framework of its views of addiction, as contained in the following statement:

> We affirm that addiction to heroin is in the same category as other addictions, and that all represent varying degrees of rebellion against God. Heroin addiction does not kill the moral sensitivities of the addict, although desire for it almost entirely eliminates a sense of moral

responsibility when the craving for narcotics is upon him. Even the most confirmed addict, however, shows evidence of his moral nature in that he has his own "commandments" of things which he will not do to obtain heroin even when in direst need. Spiritually, addicted people are empty, and they know that they are empty. After the first happy days of addiction are over, despair and meaninglessness press in upon them, offering them no hope. For a small number, rebirth in God has revolutionized their entire personalities, and they have found purpose in life without narcotics. These rebirths point to the possibility of all types of addicted people finding new life in giving their lives to God.[14]

The committee provides the following specific services:

1. Referral to hospitals.
2. Advice and help to those returning from hospitals and prisons.
   (a) Help and advice on finding jobs.
   (b) Family counseling.
   (c) Psychiatric counseling, if indicated and desired.
   (d) Help in finding food, clothing, and shelter for those who have none. The parish pays for these things if necessary.
   (e) Help in use of leisure time.
   (f) Spiritual and pastoral counseling.
3. Help in going through the medical withdrawal program.
4. Legal advice, both to those in difficulty with the law and their families.
5. Help with problems faced by and with other agencies such as the Department of Welfare, the courts, probation, and parole.

The services are free to anyone who wants to use them, but usually no one outside the parish area applies. The committee's immediate concern is the people within the confines of its parish area, although information will be given over the phone to individuals and agencies trying to find ways of helping addicted persons who live in East Harlem.

The services are provided as long as persons want to make use of them. The committee has helped some persons for as long as ten years. The committee usually does not make any attempt to follow persons who move out of the neighborhood.

The Narcotics Committee has helped many addicted persons in East Harlem. It is one of the front lines against the narcotics problem.

14 Norman Eddy, unpublished paper, "A Christian View of Addicts to Narcotics," New York, 1963.

Summary

During the past six years I have talked to or corresponded with leaders in each of these agencies. Each agency has a unique approach to treatment and, according to its reports, has been successful in meeting the needs of people addicted to narcotic drugs.

Perhaps each agency believes its approach to be superior to other approaches. However, I do not think any agency would minimize or deny the many problems involved in helping people overcome the narcotic problem.

Comparative evaluation of the effectiveness of these programs with hospital and correctional programs cannot be done. Addicted persons entering different types of programs probably have markedly different characteristics, especially in motivation and readiness to change. The Federal hospitals and correctional agencies admit a large proportion of addicts involuntarily. In contrast, Teen Challenge accepts only one of ten applicants, and Synanon rejects a substantial number of applicants.

In my experience, what works with one person might not work with the next. Persons in the field who have been working with addicted persons for many years report hearing of some very strange, but effective, approaches to treatment.

It seems to me that we need to gather all the data we can, examine it carefully, and share the knowledge with each other.

CHAPTER NINE

CONTINUING PASTORAL RELATIONSHIP

The initial contact between the minister and the addict will often, with the assistance of a physician, result in the hospitalization of the addict. In the hospital, the addict can be medically withdrawn from drugs. Sometimes it may take pressure to get the addict to go to the hospital. He may want to quit drugs but feels that he can't stand the discomfort of withdrawal. Once in a hospital, he will be withdrawn—provided he stays long enough. Usually a week to ten days is sufficient to accomplish physical withdrawal. If the addict is hospitalized in one of our two Federal hospitals, he should be encouraged to remain in the hospital at least five to ten months.

During the period of hospitalization, the minister should continue his relationship with the addict. He may write to the patient as often as he wants. An occasional visit would be a boost to the patient's morale. When the minister visits, he may learn of many of the patient's attitudes about his present situation as well as his plans for the future. The minister may notice that the patient is very confident of his abilities. He may claim to understand his problems completely, to need only to leave the hospital to begin to practice the things he knows that he should do (namely, to let narcotic drugs alone and begin to stand on his own feet). The minister may also notice that the patient may be a little grandiose about the type of work he plans to do. Hopefully, the minister will be optimistic in his forecast for the addict, but he should also represent reality. Addicts are great for evading reality. One of the reasons they use drugs is to avoid facing trying situations. The minister's patient insistence that the addict face reality will not only encourage him but will let him know that someone else is looking into reality with him and that he is not alone.

The minister should keep in close contact with the staff of the hospital. Often patients will decide to leave the hospital before the staff believes they are ready. They will tell the staff that they have someone outside who is going to get a good job for them and give them a place to stay; before the staff can verify the plans, the patient checks out. He then goes to his outside contact and tells them the hospital discharged him and that he needs help. Many headaches can be spared the counselor if he works closely with the hospital in making plans for the patient. The patient will not like this situation. He will feel that others are usurping his rights. Perhaps he suspects a conspiracy against him. In actuality, he finds himself in a situation in which he cannot manipulate others, and he feels uncomfortable. He would rather be the liaison himself between the hospital and the outside contact. Then he could plan things the way he wants to.

Sooner or later, with or without planning, the addict returns to the community. Regardless of what the addict may say, he is probably not in as good control of his problems as he would like to think. Most experts agree that hospitalization of the addict is not enough.

"Hospitalization is not enough, because upon discharge the patient often finds himself in the same painful environment that helped lead him to addiction. The return of a treated addict to an environment where drugs are available is almost a certain return to addiction. Some type of after-care program extending for a long period, and perhaps indefinitely, seems needed to strengthen and train the addicted person for normal living. One problem: typically, the addicted person has been treated as an outcast and even a criminal and he feels he will continue to be treated that way."[1]

The hospital (1) withdraws the addict from narcotic drugs, (2) keeps him in a drug-free environment for a time, (3) provides an opportunity for the addict to examine his reasons for using drugs, (4) provides opportunity for him to strengthen himself through participation in psychotherapy, education, vocational training, social and recreational activity, (5) provides opportunity for religious development, (6) attempts to help him to rebuild some of the broken relationships between him and his family and the community. The real test comes, however, when the addict leaves the structured hospital community to try to live a responsible life in the larger society with-

[1] Yahraes, op. cit., p. 21.

out resorting to the use of narcotic drugs. To assume that the addict is permanently "cured" is a mistake. The addict himself may have to be reminded of the many pitfalls that lie before him. One of the biggest will be that not everything will go the way he wants it to. He will have to learn to live with disappointment. This chapter will be directed toward the major needs of the addict as he tries to reconstruct his life after hospitalization.

Counselor

The former addict returning to society may like to think he is mature enough to handle his problems alone. The number of addicts who return to the use of drugs and eventually get into trouble seems to indicate otherwise.

"The addicted person does best when he has some type of authority to bolster him; like an adolescent, he wants limits set for him. Possibly this authority can be effectively exerted by an experienced worker in the field of addiction—physician, pastor, social worker—who is genuinely interested in the addicted person, has time and patience to help him, and wins his respect. Possibly the authority must have the force of the law behind it for best results."[2] Another authority on drug addiction, Dr. George Parkhurst, said, "When the patient leaves the hospital, he should be supervised by a warm, accepting person who is able to see him often at first. One who detects if he returns to drugs, yet able to empathize with him and help him grow through the periods of frustration and learn to handle his problem without drugs."[3] The former addict may do better if he has one counselor rather than several. If he has to report to several he will probably be tempted to manipulate and use one against the other. The counselor should be available to the former addict twenty-four hours per day.

The pastoral counselor should be optimistic about the rehabilitation of addicts, yet be realistic enough to recognize that the addict will occasionally slip.

[2] Ibid.
[3] George Parkhurst, unpublished manuscript, "Problems in the Treatment of Drug Addiction."

One of the most significant research projects in the field of narcotic addiction resulted in the following observation:

"It is important to view addiction as a chronic illness in which periodic abstinence of even a few weeks or months is considered a boon to patient, family, and community. Total abstinence over extended periods of time may be a goal beyond realization for most of these patients. Even if abstinence from drugs is established as a primary goal, it can rarely be achieved in a straight line. If it happens at all, it will occur through a series of stops and starts with allowance made for an indefinite number of relapses, slips, and acting-out behavior. Addicts continually fall back on drugs in an effort to achieve some balance in their lives, to bolster their strength in meeting the strains of living and coping with people and social situations."[4] The pastor therefore, not only has to be available at any time, but also has to be prepared to face setbacks in the person's rehabilitation. The part the minister plays might best be summarized in the words, ". . . and underneath are the everlasting arms." The minister's task is to support the person with one hand and push him with the other, but not so hard and abruptly that he forces him out of the hand that is holding him. The minister must remember that in most instances the addict is at once a grown man and a little boy. He must be respected as a man and treated as a man; yet at the same time the minister needs to be constantly aware of the little boy who may be trying desperately to be a man, but having a difficult time doing it.

Usually the counselor will not engage the former addict in an intensive counseling relationship. The individual may not be able to stand a very close relationship with any person—at least not close enough for psychotherapy as it is usually understood. What may be more effective is for the minister to actually supervise the former addict in a directive and authoritative manner. Tell the addict things he needs to know and to do. Tell him things not to do. Follow him carefully to see that he completes projects he starts. In essence, the minister serves as a good, understanding, authority figure, who helps the individual work out and follow through on everyday responsibility.

[4] Leon Brill, *Rehabilitation in Drug Addiction*, U.S. Public Service Publication No. 1013 (Washington, D.C.: Government Printing Office, 1963), p. 9.

A Place to Stay

Upon discharge from the hospital the addict has to go somewhere. He usually goes to the place he knows best. This is also the environment in which he found drugs. Should the treated addict return to that same environment where drugs are available, he is likely to return to addiction. The minister who is helping the addict may be fully aware of the danger of his slipping into the old patterns should he return to the old environment. What are the other possibilities?

With the minister.   Some ministers have taken addicts into their homes. Ministers who do this should be aware that events such as the following may occur:

A minister who took an addict into his home had maintained a relationship with the addict for several months prior to his discharge from the hospital. The minister was to help the addict secure a job and eventually a place to stay but, in the meantime, had offered him the hospitality of his own home. The second night the minister was awakened shortly after midnight by noises that seemed to be coming from the kitchen. He rose from his bed and went into the kitchen. He found his house guest in the kitchen, busily cooking something on the stove. The addict was boiling down some paregoric. He had gone to a nearby drugstore and purchased it earlier in the day while the minister was away visiting a sick parishioner.

Some ministers who have taken previously addicted persons into their home for a time report the experience to have been successful. The former addict remained with the minister until he found work, received a pay check, and was financially able to be independent. Some report a continuation of relationship with the addict by frequent visits from the addict to the minister. In a few instances the person became a regular attender in the minister's church. Reports such as these are encouraging, but I am inclined to believe they are in the minority.

With parents.   Many addicts who return to society after a stay in the hospital plan to live with parents until they can get adjusted. Unless the person has achieved a significant emotional change as an outcome of treatment, returning to live with parents may revive or intensify previous conflicts. This is especially likely to occur if adverse parental attitudes or conflicts that prompted drug use still exist. For example, inconsistent parental attitudes prompt emotional difficulty in individuals.

While in the hospital, the addicts may tend to repress the stress and tension they experienced in their home situation prior to hospitalization. They forget their feelings of rebellion or depression and frustration, and how these feelings helped to widen the gap of misunderstanding between them and their families. Nor are they aware that the family probably still maintains the same image of them, that is, a hostile, manipulative, self-centered person who always wants his way. Almost always the family will give the addict another chance, but its members do not always believe his story of being a new person until they see some concrete changes.

The former addict who has some superficial awareness of himself may feel competent to handle himself in any situation. What often happens is that, upon his return home, the addict attempts to manipulate his people into seeing him in a new light. Sometimes families who have the experience of seeing a son or daughter recurrently addicted and recurrently institutionalized over a number of years become disillusioned and doubtful of promises a person makes. They don't hear what he is saying because they perceive the manipulative behavior and respond to it. They ask him to prove that he is different. Seeing that his story is not believed, he becomes angry and frustrated. He thinks he has really tried, but is not getting any support from his people. Once he becomes frustrated, he must find a way to relieve tension. He knows what will work. He knows where to find it. His people begin to notice his irritability. They know what comes next and they begin to get panicky. Instead of handling his anxiety, and understanding the anxiety of his people, he runs to find relief for himself. After he has fixed, he feels guilty. He had planned to do so well. But he failed. He decides there is no hope for him. The fault, he thinks, is with those who would not understand him. He tells himself that if they would only listen to him and do what he wanted them to do everything would be all right.

Some addicts want to get away from home. They realize the depth of chronic or recurrent frustration, anxiety, or conflict they have experienced while living with parents. Any event that brings feelings of frustration, anger, depression, whether it be in the family, job, or relationships, increases the possibility of his return to drug use. A significant proportion of former addicts are prompted to return to drug use for this reason.

Halfway Houses.   Some believe the best way for the addict to become readjusted to society is to live for a time in a Halfway House. The Halfway House is actually an extension of an institution. Persons soon to be released from institutions are moved into quarters in the community. They stay there until they are due to be released. These houses are staffed by trained persons who provide support and counsel. The addicts work at jobs in the community during the day and live in the house at night. In the evenings they may be involved in group discussion on difficulties and problems that arise as they try to adjust themselves to regular work and society.

At present, only a few Halfway Houses are in existence. They have not been in operation long enough to provide conclusive data for evaluation. It is my opinion that Halfway Houses may be one of the better solutions to the problem of assisting addicted persons to adjust to the community.

Nursing home or hospital commitment.   There is a special problem in finding a home for some of the older addicts. There are quite a few in this group who check into and out of the Federal hospitals several times a year. Many of these patients have used drugs for twenty years or more. In addition to their addiction to drugs, many are physically unable to work at a regular job and care for themselves. Others who are without any vocational skill cannot find employment. Some have a meager pension as their only means of support.

These patients are generally unable to respond to any active hospital treatment program and are only provided with physical withdrawal, domiciliary and medical care. They usually stay in the hospital just long enough to be physically withdrawn from drugs (a few weeks). Outside the hospital, these addicts usually live in an inadequate boarding house or hotel. It is not uncommon for three or four of these older addicts to live together at a boarding house.

The minister may have cases such as these called to his attention. The addict may be the relative of a member of his church. The relative may seek the minister's guidance about what can be done for the addicted person. Probably the elderly addict lived for a time in the home with the relative, but the experience proved to be unsatisfactory. Extremely dependent, and sometimes very demanding, some of these older addicts can become very annoying to relatives.

In some instances, care in a nursing home has been a solution. However, nursing homes can be expensive, and there is often nothing to keep the elderly addict from walking away from the home should he desire.

Admission to a state hospital is another possibility, but this will depend upon the laws of the state and upon the willingness of the person to accept hospitalization. I would recommend that the minister make information available to people, but that he not urge any particular move. The minister will often be more effective in assisting with such problems if he centers his attention upon the relatives. His best opportunity for helping will be in supporting the relatives as they make positive decisions for the continued care of the aging addict.

Work

Finding work for a former addict is no simple task. The minister who uses his influence to assist the person in securing work will probably want to inform the employer of the addiction problem. This is done only with the permission of the former addict. The minister has an obligation to be honest with the employer, but this sometimes makes getting the job difficult. Many companies have a policy that prohibits the hiring of an addict. People often are afraid of hiring persons who have had a problem with drugs. It may at times be helpful for the minister to obtain work for the addict. The minister will help the addict more effectively if he will give the addict psychological support and advice so that the person can obtain employment on his own. This tends to preserve and promote the sense of independence of the person and makes him less dependent upon somebody else.

There will be those who have no problem finding employment. Medical specialists and others in the professional groups, such as lawyers, musicians, and engineers, have usually established themselves already. In many instances, their addiction is known only to their immediate families and their physicians. As far as their employers and other interested people are concerned, they may be getting a checkup or taking a rest or an extended vacation. Almost everyone in this group returns to his home and job with very little difficulty. It is with this group, incidentally, that treatment seems to be the most successful. The hospital is successful in the sense that the patient returns to his community and seldom returns to the hospital for further treatment.

It is usually not difficult for the skilled craftsman to find work. Some skilled craftsmen who have been hospitalized for addiction claimed to have used drugs while they were employed. They said that so long as they took their drugs at regular intervals they were able to perform acceptable work. Some said that their employers knew that they were addicted but didn't seem to care as long as their work was performed accurately. They went on to say, however, that when their supply of drugs was exhausted they would have to leave their jobs in order to procure the dose they needed. Since employers did not understand why they had to leave work in the middle of the day for no apparent reason, they usually fired the addict.

Others have said that their biggest problem was the police. They claimed the police would come to their places of employment, ask them questions about whether or not they were using drugs, and sometimes search them. Many addicts claim to have been fired because of the harassment of police. They said the employers didn't mind their addiction but considered their being constantly under surveillance of the police to be bad for the morale of the other workers. It is quite possible that addicts exaggerate police harassment in order to conceal their own work instability.

The majority of addicts I have known are vocationally unskilled. They would not fit into a labor class because most of them have never worked for any extended period at a legitimate enterprise to sustain themselves. Usually high school dropouts with a desire to get nice, expensive things immediately, plus a drug habit (which in itself is very expensive), addicts look for the quickest and easiest way to make money. Their work often gets them arrested.

Some employment agencies report that some former addicts referred to employers never appeared for work. For example: An agency agreed to assist in the placement of an unskilled former addict. The addict was given a job and was told to report the following morning at 8:00 A.M., ready to go to work. At 8:00 A.M. the addict had not reported to work. At midmorning the employer called the agency and told them not to send him anybody else that would not even report or call in. It was learned later that the addict had left the city during the night and by morning was several hundred miles away. Within a few days he was in jail for vagrancy and suspicion of narcotic sales.

Other employment agencies report no difficulty in finding a job for an addict but state that addicts seem to have trouble taking orders and getting along with their bosses. This is the picture we frequently see in the hospital setting. The addict's inability to tolerate frustration causes him to run at the least encounter. In the hospital, he will ask for a job change if he has trouble with a boss. Outside the hospital, he will just walk off a job. He may walk off without explanation, which ruins his opportunity ever to return to that particular job.

Unless the addict has a job he really likes—one that makes him feel creative and important, and pays very well—his work record will probably be off and on. If the minister is helping him to find work, the minister may get very provoked at his constant quitting. The minister may have to confront the addict with his limited skills and abilities and his job instability and attempt to help him by discussion, rather than by means of direct intervention.

Relationships

The former addict returning to society needs relationships. Unless he has made significant changes during treatment, he may continue the sort of relationships he maintained prior to his hospitalization. It was pointed out in an earlier chapter that addicts usually have experienced a conflict in their maternal relationship. One evidence of their seeking maternal gratification is revealed by instances of addicts marrying older women. Addicts who seek out older women probably do so for an exploitive relationship and for convenience. Some authorities say the addict is looking for a mother who will give him all the things he demands and also love him in a crippling way. When he finds such a woman, he will stay with her so long as she provides a nice place for him to stay and money for him to spend on himself—

and does not make any demands of him in terms of being productive and responsible.

Should the former addict involve himself in such a relationship after discharge from the hospital, the possibility of his returning to drug use is increased.

Some former addicts think changing their environment resolves their difficulty in relationships with people. When addicts say, "I'm going to change my environment," they usually mean that they plan to move from one geographic area to another. We know this has helped some people to stay off drugs, but it does not work for everyone. Addicts may entertain the notion that moving to a different neighborhood or city resolves their problems and permits them to start life anew. They do not realize that they can find their old environment in almost any city. When an addict gets to a new town he frequents the bars and hangouts of people with whom he can relate. Thinking of himself as an outcast of society, and usually treated as one, he goes where he can find people who are sympathetic to his problem and will accept him, even if it is to use him for meeting their needs. He may aspire to the life of a square, but he does not believe it will really work for him.

One addict said, "That other life is all I know; I can make it with junkies, prostitutes, pimps, and thieves. I know they are bad, but I'm bad, too. We understand each other. It's live and let live. Those righteous people scare me. I just don't trust them. Maybe it's me that I don't trust. I just don't know how to act around them. I don't do the things they do. I never watch ball games—or whatever those people do."

It is easy to see that the addict with this attitude will have a difficult time integrating himself into the acceptable society of the squares. Becoming a square troubles the addict. He is afraid that he is different from everyone else. To the addict, being different means being alone. Usually he has been a loner. He probably has ruined most of his relationships, but this does not mean that he enjoys the loneliness. I think it is more accurate to say of the addict that he is a lonely person who really does not know how to make and keep a genuine relationship. Telling the addict about relationships is of very little consequence. He has to be shown.

The relationship with the minister will be an important one, but the addict needs more than one relationship. In fact, some addicts have difficulty relating to one person, especially to a person in authority. Addicts seem to feel more at ease in a group. They need a group that is warm and encouraging. Perhaps one reason Narcotics Anonymous and Alcoholics Anonymous are so effective with these individuals is the acceptance found at meetings of these organizations. It should be pointed out that Narcotics Anonymous and Alcoholics Anonymous do not work for everyone, but do help many. It is also worth noting that Narcotics Anonymous and Alcoholics Anonymous usually have some sort of meeting every evening.

To illustrate the need of addicts for group relationships, let us consider the following story related to me by a minister who was very interested in an addict:

When he came out of the hospital he was so enthusiastic. He was filled with a joy I have seldom seen in people. He couldn't seem to wait until we had a church service so that he could join our congregation. He did join at the first service after his release from the hospital. He never missed a service after that for some time. He told me repeatedly how much he enjoyed the services. He said that while in church he felt at home. He would call me several times a week to see if a special meeting was being held. After a time he did not call so frequently. Then I noticed that he would occasionally miss a service. Then, before long, he did not come at all. I asked around about him and found that he had started using drugs again. I discussed this with some of the people at the church. Of course we are not experts, but we suspect that if we had something going at the church every night to occupy his time and provide him with friendship he might never have returned to drugs.

It is impossible to know whether or not this addict would have eventually returned to drugs anyway. However, leaders in Alcoholics Anonymous tell me that for many alcoholics, remaining sober depends on regular attendance at A.A. meetings. Some say they need a meeting every day. Others say they can usually tell when a member starts drinking again by his absence from meetings.

Attending some sort of meeting is important for the addict, too. He either finds the support he needs in relationships or runs to drugs. I would suggest that the best place for the addict to start relationships would be in Narcotics Anonymous or Alcoholics Anonymous. In almost every town of any size there is an Alcoholics Anonymous Club. The addict will find persons in the club who understand him and have some awareness of the problem with which he is dealing. Many persons who have been addicted report that, even though they eventually became socially adjusted and belonged to several organizations, including the church, they still maintained their relationship with Alcoholics Anonymous. One person said, "When I get to feeling I want to be with someone who will let me just be plain old me, I go to Alcoholics Anonymous." It is a blessing that such an environment exists so that people who feel unacceptable can find acceptance. I should hope that people with these feelings might find an accepting environment in the church.

CHAPTER TEN

CONCLUSION

The minister may play an important role in the rehabilitation of the narcotic addict. The role will depend upon the time the minister can give, his own personality makeup and temperament, and his understanding of the complex problems in narcotic addiction. Last, but very important, the addict must trust the minister. Initially, this trust may be a fleeting and insubstantial one, and it may be an exploitive relationship.

The addict may come to the minister's attention in a number of ways. He may be referred or brought by a member of the family. Some agency that knows the minister's ability in counseling may make the referral. The addict may come on his own. If the addict is addicted at the initial contact, the minister should call a physician, who can determine the actual extent of addiction and can arrange for immediate hospitalization of the addict.

During hospitalization, the minister can continue his relationship with the addict. Whether he is hospitalized in a local general hospital or in a special narcotic hospital, the addict needs a relationship with someone who can be a friend and offer encouragement. If the addict is hospitalized in a local general hospital, the physician will probably want to keep him in treatment at least a week or two. Hospitalization in a special narcotic hospital will probably be of longer duration. In either case, the minister should encourage the addict to stay in treatment until he is released by the physician.

The minister may find himself to be the main resource in the former addict's life after discharge. The person may look to him for advice, counsel, and support. The task will be time-consuming. It may involve planning a step-by-step program with the addict, as he prepares to rehabilitate himself. The minister's constant prodding may be required to encourage the former addict to follow through on the plans.

The minister will have to be available to do trouble-shooting work day or night. Regularly scheduled appointments may have little meaning to the addict. The relationship with the minister will continue from one crisis to the next. If the person calls the minister with a problem in the middle of the night, and the minister tells him that he will have to wait until morning before he can discuss the matter with him, a counselee may be lost. The addict cannot tolerate very much anxiety. If the person calls and says that he is anxious, the minister should listen. If the minister postpones the talk, the former addict will seek relief elsewhere. He knows where he can find immediate relief. He is also afraid he will run to that relief. His call to the minister means he is trying; the minister should compliment him for using good judgment and then be available to help work out the problem, whatever it may be.

Any relationship with a former addict will be stormy. He will constantly test and threaten and manipulate. The minister must be prepared to meet these situations with understanding, love, and firmness. The minister must also be prepared if the person slips and uses narcotics. More than likely there will be many starts and stops. However, as the relationship weathers them out, the number of slips will, hopefully, decrease.

The former addict not only needs the relationship with a person, he also needs to grow in his understanding of God. He probably will not be able to comprehend all the minister would like to tell him about God until he begins to experience something good and genuine in his relationship with people. I have known some addicts who had a sort of religious experience and began to practice and preach religion to anyone who would listen. Although they were able to stay off drugs (and this is no simple matter), their basic attitude toward people did not seem to change. They were not able to trust anyone. They relied solely on their new relationship with God to give their lives meaning and remained aloof from all other relationships. It occurs to me that this was their problem in the beginning, for which, in seeking a solution, they tried drugs for awhile. The change we want to bring about in the lives of the people we counsel is one that incorporates harmony, and mutual respect and trust of others. In my opinion, this is not taught—it is shown. If the former addict is to learn this new concept, the minister will have to show him.

The low economic, depressed areas of our large cities, especially New York, Los Angeles, Chicago, and Detroit, produce the overwhelming majority of the narcotic addicts. There are indications, however, that the problem is also noticeable in the better suburban areas. I believe that the problem is not in the place so much, nor in the drug itself; the problem is in the people. Disruption of family life, with consequent anguish, despair, and conflict, represents one root of the problem. When something is basically wrong with a plant, the symptom that first appears is a discoloring of the leaves. When something is amiss in a family structure, the symptoms usually manifest themselves in the children. The majority of narcotic addicts have begun drug use in their late teens or early twenties, and perhaps they are the leaves of a sick plant. Treatment of a plant means careful examination of its total situation. As the total plant is treated, and health is restored, proper coloring returns to the leaves. Many have been telling us for some time that we do not actually help our youth until we involve their families in treatment also. We do not solve the addiction problem by isolating the addicts and treating them as if they were different creatures from the rest of us. In order to treat them properly, we must involve the total family—perhaps the community—in a re-evaluation of purposes, goals, and relationships with people.

The minister counsels the individual. He is also a prophet who speaks out against existing destructive conditions in society and offers a message that can bring healing and hope. The task of the minister is to look carefully at the problems of our day that manifest themselves in the lives of our youth, and to bring to the people a message from on high that will cure our ills and restore us to health and to life.

Drug addiction especially affects depressed minority groups, noticeably Negroes, Puerto Ricans, and Mexicans. The minister, with many others, should participate in efforts to reduce human disorganization and human despair arising from adverse social conditions.

The problem of addiction is complex, requiring all the human skills available. It also takes the Holy Spirit, Who, given the best efforts of man, blesses them and uses them for His own purposes, namely, releasing the captives and healing the broken in spirit.

BIBLIOGRAPHY

Books

Alcoholics Anonymous. New York: Alcoholics Anonymous, Inc., 1955.

ANSLINGER, H. J. and WILLIAM F. TOMPKINS, *The Traffic in Narcotics.* New York: Funk & Wagnalls Co., 1953.

AUSUBEL, D. P., *Drug Addiction: Physiological, Psychological and Sociological Aspects.* New York: Random House, Inc., 1958.

CASRIEL, DANIEL, *So Fair a House: The Story of Synanon.* Englewood Cliffs, N.J.: Prentice-Hall, Inc., 1963.

MARKS, JAN, *Doctor Purgatory.* New York: The Citadel Press, 1959.

RASOR, ROBERT W., "Narcotic Addicts: Personality Characteristics in Hospital Treatment," in *Problems of Addiction and Habituation,* eds., PAUL H. HOCH and JOSEPH ZUBIN. New York: Grune & Stratton, Inc., 1958.

VOGEL, V. H. and D. W. MAURER, *Narcotics and Narcotic Addiction.* Springfield, Ill.: Charles C. Thomas, Publisher, 1954.

VOGEL, V. H. and VIRGINIA VOGEL, *Facts About Narcotics.* Chicago: Science Research Associates, 1951.

WILKERSON, DAVID, *The Cross and the Switch Blade.* New York: Bernard Geis Associates, 1963.

YOST, ORIN ROSS, *The Bane of Drug Addiction.* New York: The Macmillan Company, 1954.

Government Publications

BRILL, LEON, *Rehabilitation in Drug Addiction,* U.S. Public Health Service Publication No. 1013. Washington, D.C.: Government Printing Office, 1963.

ISBELL, HARRIS, *What to Know About Drug Addiction,* U.S. Public

Health Service Publication No. 94. Washington, D.C.: Government Printing Office, 1958.

President's Advisory Commission on Narcotic and Drug Abuse, Final Report. Washington, D.C.: Government Printing Office, 1963.

Proceedings, White House Conference on Narcotic and Drug Abuse. Washington, D.C.: Government Printing Office, 1963.

YAHRAES, HERBERT, *Narcotic Drug Addiction,* U.S. Public Health Service Publication No. 1021. Washington 25, D.C.: Government Printing Office.

Periodicals

BERLINER, ARTHUR K., "The Helping Process in a Hospital for Narcotic Addicts," *Federal Probation* XXVI, No. 3 (September 1962), 57.

BURNS, KATHY, "Escape From Drugs," *The Dallas Times Herald Sunday Magazine,* February 24, 1963.

CHAPMAN, KENNETH W., "The Addict and the Community," *Federal Probation,* XXI, No. 1 (March, 1957), 41–44.

COREY, STEPHEN J., "A Chaplain Looks at Drug Addiction," *Federal Probation,* XV, No. 3 (September, 1951), 17.

JORJORIAN, ARMEN D., "Drug Addiction and the Pastor," *Pastoral Psychology,* II, No. 21 (February, 1952), 25.

LOWRY, JAMES V., "The Hospital Treatment of the Narcotic Addict," *Federal Probation,* XX, No. 20 (December, 1956), 42.

WIKLER, A. and R. W. RASOR, "Psychiatric Aspects of Drug Addiction," *American Journal of Medicine,* XIV, No. 5 (1953), 566–70.

INDEX